Warships, U-Boats & Liners

Title page image: A few months after the sinking of the *Lusitania* the German satirical medallist Karl Goetz produced a medal intended to castigate the British for their disregard for possible civilian casualties in sending the *Lusitania* through a 'war zone'. Unfortunately for Goetz, he took the date of the sinking from an incorrect news report and as a result the medal bears the date 5th May, instead of 7th May. Inevitably, the British acquired a copy and over 300,000 copies were produced, along with a leaflet explaining that this was proof of Germany's intention to sink the *Lusitania*, without any regard for the possible loss of non-combatants' lives.

Warships, U-Boats & Liners

A Guide to Shipwrecks Mapped in Irish Waters by the
Irish National Seabed Survey and INFOMAR Mapping Projects

Karl Brady, Charise McKeon, James Lyttleton, Ian Lawler

With contributions by
Stuart Bennett, Eibhlín Doyle, Connie Kelleher, Koen Verbruggen,
Cormac Lowth, Erica McCarthy, JJ McDermott, Pilar Martin Bayo,
Tony Roche, Barry McGill, Sarah Fawsitt, Roy Stokes, Brian MacSharry,
Stewart Andrews, Tony Ryan and Fionnbarr Moore

BAILE ÁTHA CLIATH
ARNA FHOILSIÚ AG OIFIG AN tSOLÁTHAIR
Le ceannach díreach ón
OIFIG DHÍOLTA FOILSEACHÁN RIALTAS,
TEACH SUN ALLIANCE, SRÁID THEACH LAIGHEAN, BAILE ÁTHA CLIATH 2
nó tríd an bpost ó
FOILSEACHÁN RIALTAS, AN RANNÓG POST-TRÁCHTA,
AONAD 20 PÁIRC MIONDÍOLA COIS LOCHA, CLÁR CHLAINNE MHUIRIS, CONTAE MHAIGH EO
(TEIL. (01) 6476834 NÓ GLAOCH AITIUIL 1890 213434. FAX. (01) 6476843 NÓ 094 9378964.
Riomhphost: pubsales@opw.ie) nó trí aon díoltóir leabhar.

_____

DUBLIN
PUBLISHED BY THE STATIONERY OFFICE
To be purchased directly from the
GOVERNMENT PUBLICATIONS SALES OFFICE,
SUN ALLIANCE HOUSE, MOLESWORTH STREET, DUBLIN 2,
or by mail order from
GOVERNMENT PUBLICATIONS, POSTAL TRADE SECTION,
UNIT 20 LAKESIDE RETAIL PARK, CLAREMORRIS, CO. MAYO
(Tel: (01) 6476834 or LoCall: 1890 213434. Fax: (01) 647 6843 or 094 9378964.
Email: pubsales@opw.ie) or through any bookseller.

Price: €25

© Government of Ireland 2012
ISBN: 9781406427035
Designed and typeset by VERMILLON
Copy-edited by Rachel Pierce at Verba Editing House
Printed by Castle Print (Galway) Ltd.

Contents

Below: *Illustrated London News* engraving of the salvage operations on the wreck of HMS *Vanguard*. Difficult diving conditions restricted the salvage work to the recovery of a limited amount of the vessel's fittings. (Ian Lawler Collection)

Acknowledgments

This publication is the result of ongoing collaboration between the National Monuments Service (NMS) and the Geological Survey of Ireland (GSI) in identifying shipwrecks surveyed during the Irish National Seabed Survey (INSS) and the INFOMAR mapping project. The success of the project was made possible through the hard work of the various surveyors, data processors and crews on board the *Celtic Explorer*, *Celtic Voyager*, RV *Keary* and RV *Geo*, who have been tirelessly mapping and surveying the Irish seabed since 1999.

Thanks are due to all staff members, past and present, of INFOMAR and the INSS, both from the Geological Survey of Ireland and the Marine Institute. In particular, thanks are due to Sean Cullen of the GSI, who did the initial collation of the dataset of shipwrecks mapped during the INSS. This underpinned the work that followed on the shipwreck database for INSS and INFOMAR. Special thanks are due to Fionnbarr Moore and Koen Verbruggen for their support, advice and encouragement, especially during the final stages of the production of this publication. Thanks also to the UK Hydrographic Office for the provision of information and data from its shipwreck database.

Many people assisted in the compilation and production of this book in various ways: all the staff of the National Monuments Service who assisted at various levels with the production of the inventory, including Brian Duffy, Terry Allen, Catriona Ryan, Connie Kelleher, Holger Schweitzer and Mark Kehoe; the staff from the Geological Survey of Ireland, including Sean Cullen; and Mick Geoghegan, Stuart Bennett and Eibhlín Doyle for their valued contribution to the project between 2000 and 2006.

Acknowledgments are due to the following institutions for permission to publish copyrighted material: the National Library of Ireland; Diageo Ireland; the National Maritime Museum, Dún Laoghaire; the National Maritime Museum, Greenwich; the Imperial War Museum, London; the British Mercantile Marine Memorial Collection; the Museum of New Zealand, Te Papa Tongarewa; US Naval Historical Foundation; the Centre of Newfoundland Studies, Memorial University of Newfoundland; Royal Navy Submarine Museum; the Glasgow Life Archives; the U-Boot Archiv, Cuxhaven; and *The Irish Times*. Thanks must also be given to Tony Roche and Con Brogan of the Photographic Unit of the National Monuments Service for their help, supply of images and assistance with image-enhancement work.

A sincere thanks to the following individuals for contributing images: Ian Lawler; Lar Dunne; Barry McGill; Graham Stokes; Carl Douglas (www.deepsea.se); Kenneth King; Michael Charles of the British Mercantile Marine Memorial Collection; and Horst Bredow of the U-Boot Archiv.

The following individuals carried out research, made contributions to or were of general assistance in the compilation of this book: Roy Stokes; Connie Kelleher; Cormac Lowth; Tom Beurghs; Erica McCarthy; JJ McDermott; Pilar Martin Bayo; Barry McGill; Sarah Fawsitt; Roy Stokes; Brian MacSharry; Stewart Andrews; and Connie Kelleher.

Numerous people gave freely of their time and supplied much useful information during the project, including: Clement McGann; Eoghan Ganly; Roger Kirker; Sinéad Brady; Brian Shanahan; Colin Breen; Brian Murray; John Brady; Hans Heesakkers; Raymond Mijdam; Rich Stevenson; Michael McVeigh; Eoghan Kieran; Rory Quinn; Cormac Lowth; Timmy Carey; and Eoin McGarry.

Finally, thanks are due to Kevin Dunne and Anne Brady of Vermillion Design Ltd for their excellent design work in typesetting and producing this book and to Rachel Pierce of Verba Editing House for her patience and outstanding editorial skills.

Image Acknowledgments

All multibeam and sidescan sonar images used in the book are supplied by the INSS (Geological Survey of Ireland) and INFOMAR (Geological Survey of Ireland/ Marine Institute), unless otherwise stated.

Welcome Note

Minister for Arts, Heritage and the Gaeltacht

Since 1987, when the National Monuments Act was amended to afford protection to underwater wrecks over 100 years old and archaeological objects underwater, the State has been committed to developing a capacity to deal with the responsibilities resulting from such far-reaching legislative change.

Since its establishment in 1997, my Department's Underwater Archaeology Unit (UAU), which is now an integral part of the National Monuments Service, has built up an extensive archive of shipwrecks and coastal features. The UAU has also undertaken many surveys and excavations of existing and newly discovered wrecks. Most recently, the UAU has investigated a possible Spanish Armada wreck at Rutland Island in Donegal, with the aid of major logistical support from the Geological Survey of Ireland. The UAU has also just completed the recovery of an important medieval shipwreck from the River Boyne at Drogheda, which is currently being conserved by the National Museum of Ireland.

The UAU plays a key role in assessing national and international developments that impact on our underwater cultural heritage. It is also pro-active in publishing the results of its work, and this co-operative venture with the GSI is a further example of that commitment as well as a fine tribute to the benefits of inter-service co-operation and support.

Around the same time as the UAU was set up, in 1997, the GSI was initiating the Irish National Seabed Survey (INSS). From the outset there was close contact between the GSI and the UAU. As the survey progressed, it became clear that one of the significant by-products of the multibeam surveys being carried out in the deeper waters off our shores was the discovery of numerous shipwrecks, many of which had come to grief as a result of hostile action during World War I and World War II. New imagery was also captured for older wrecks, such as the French Armada frigate *La Surveillante*, which was scuttled in Bantry Bay in 1797. It

was clear to all concerned that such discoveries deserved to be published and that every effort should be made to identify the wrecks and place them in their historical context.

The wrecks identified by the INSS tell a dramatic and often terrible story of events around our coast over the centuries. These range from simple errors of judgment, with no loss of life, as in the case of the HMS *Vanguard*, which was accidentally rammed by its sister ship, HMS *Iron Duke*, in 1875, to inexplicable fires, such as that on the SS *Manchester Merchant*, the former Boer War transport vessel, which sank off Rosbehy Point in Dingle Bay in 1903. The bell from that ship is now in the Roman Catholic church in Anascaul, home of Tom Crean, famous Kerry mariner and Arctic explorer. The local bounty from the wreck was cotton and turpentine – treasure indeed!

As always, there is an unsinkable ship that sinks: in this case, the Birkenhead-built dreadnought battleship, HMS *Audacious*. Ironically, it was the first capital ship to be lost by any nation in World War I after striking a mine near Tory Island in October 1914. The *Hare* has a particular relevance to Irish history as it brought 340 tons of food to starving Dublin workers during the 1913 Lockout. One reads here also of other major losses that occurred during this period, for example the RMS *Leinster,* torpedoed off Howth Head in October 1918 with 501 lives lost and with only weeks to go to the November armistice. Most famous of all during World War I was the RMS *Lusitania,* torpedoed in 1915 off the Old Head of Kinsale with the loss of 1,198 lives. It is the first and only wreck so far protected by an Underwater Heritage Order.

The story of World War II is also brought alive in the pages of this volume. As in World War I, passenger ships were not immune from attack and one reads of the unsuspecting *Athenia*, for example, a passenger liner and the first ship sunk by submarine in World War II, just a few hours after hostilities broke out between Britain and Germany. The tragic loss of the Limerick merchant vessel, the *Kerry Head*, serves to remind us of the heroic service rendered by Irish shipping during the war years.

One could go on and reflect on all the vessels listed in this volume and the extraordinary stories they have to tell, but it would be wrong to sign off without mentioning the SS *Muirchú*. Built in Dublin in 1908, it was witness to some of the most extraordinary events in modern Irish history. Initially operating as a fishery protection cruiser, it was requisitioned by the Royal Navy, as HMY *Helga*, for anti-submarine patrol duties, shelled rebel positions in Dublin in 1916 and was also involved in rescuing 90 people from the stricken RMS *Leinster*. It transported Free State troops along the Munster coastline during the Civil War in 1923, returning to fisheries patrol duties after that, and ultimately it became the first ship of the new Irish Naval Service in 1947. If ever a ship could tell a story!

Apart from their cultural and historical importance, many of the wrecks described in this volume have an international dimension and a potential to generate tourism and stimulate local economies. With the support of responsible dive centres and local dive clubs, which form a key part of our tourism infrastructure, these wrecks can be explored now and into the distant future by visitors from home and abroad.

While the book contains a wonderful collection of maritime stories, beautifully illustrated and well researched, many of the events recounted have a tragic and cruel quality that has often left a sad legacy for communities and individuals. The images of these wrecks now resting quietly on the seabed are in stark contrast to the tumultuous events in which they were caught up. In a way, they resonate all the more strongly for that.

The sea has always invoked fear and respect, and in the Irish tradition there was no exception. The words of the Kerry poet, Muiris Mac Dáibhí Dhuibh Mac Gearailt, praying for safe passage when voyaging to Spain with the exiled Gaelic Irish Lord, Domhnall Cam Ó Súilleabháin Béarra, in the early years of the 17th century are as apt today as they ever were:

> *Beannaigh an longsa, a Chríost cháidh,*
> *an tsíon, an tonn-sa, 's an tír;*
> *bíd t'aingil 'na gcléith dár gcóir*
> *is róinn mar sgéith ndaingin dín.*

> *Bless our good ship, O Lord of heavenly hosts;*
> *Save us from winds, from waves and dangerous coasts;*
> *Let thy celestial angels spread their shields*
> *And guard us safely through these azure fields.*[1]

Jimmy Deenihan

Jimmy Deenihan TD
Minister for Arts, Heritage and the Gaeltacht

[1] O'Rahilly, T.F. (ed.) *Measgra Dánta: Miscellaneous Irish Poems*, Part II, Cork, 1927, pp.130–32:198-200. Eighteenth-century translator unknown, but written in the hand of the poet and scribe Micheál Ó Longáin.

Welcome Note

Minister of State at the Department of Communications, Energy and Natural Resources

For the past 12 years, Ireland's offshore waters and coastal seas have been subject to one of the largest seabed surveys in the world. Integrated Mapping for the Sustainable Development of Ireland's Marine Resource (INFOMAR) is Ireland's national marine mapping programme, the follow-on project to the Irish National Seabed Survey (INSS), which began in 1999. The INFOMAR project is a joint venture of the Geological Survey of Ireland, Department of Communications, Energy and Natural Resources, and the Marine Institute, Department of Agriculture, Fisheries and Food. This project is currently scheduled to run for a 20 year period (2006–2026), with priority in the first ten years being given to mapping 26 bays and three offshore areas. Previously INSS (to 2005), managed by GSI, mapped all of the deeper waters (>200m) and delivered a national asset that provided Ireland with a dataset to underpin economic, environmental, infrastructural, social and policy strategies. There now remains a crucially important body of work for INFOMAR to follow up on, the aim of which is to map commercially valuable inshore and other waters outside the scope of that achieved by the INSS.

INFOMAR concentrates on creating a range of integrated mapping products of the physical, chemical and biological features of the seabed in the near-shore area, and making this data available free online. This data delivery strategy is intended to promote value-added products and contribute to the national development effort, and to Ireland's future socio-economic prosperity. This data is also being incorporated into various EU projects, generating new datasets on a European level, to inform planning decisions at the highest levels.

Surveys are carried out using a range of research ships and aircraft, including the GSI's inshore launches RV *Keary* and RV *Geo*, the Marine Institute's RV *Celtic Explorer* and RV *Celtic Voyager* and Airborne LIDAR [Laser – light

detection and ranging]. The programme principally uses ship-mounted acoustic multibeam sonar and geophysical technology to provide vital information on water depth for safe shipping, as well as to analyse the properties of the seabed for information that can guide fishing, ocean renewable development, environmental protection and marine archaeology.

Since the commencement of the INSS in 1999, a comprehensive database of the shipwrecks that have been mapped has been collated. It is this dataset that has provided in-depth information of known and unknown shipwrecks in Irish waters and has led to collaborative work with the Underwater Archaeology Unit (National Monuments Service, Department of Arts, Heritage and the Gaeltacht). The mapped data has, in most cases, greatly improved the accuracy of the charted positions for many of these shipwrecks, some of which are world renowned, as well as providing never before seen images of how these shipwrecks lie on the seafloor today. This dataset will contribute significantly to the development of Irish marine cultural heritage and also to the safety of navigation in Irish waters, delivered through updated Admiralty charts produced by the UK Hydrographic Office.

This comprehensive guide to shipwrecks mapped in Irish waters brings together factual archaeological information with state-of-the-art bathymetric imagery to highlight sixty of the more important shipwrecks mapped in Irish waters during the INSS and INFOMAR. It is hoped that this book will be essential reading to those with an interest in Irish maritime history, in particular shipwrecks, and will provide an insight into the history surrounding these vessels and, ultimately, how they met their fate.

Fergus O'Dowd

Fergus O'Dowd TD
Minister of State at the Department of Communications, Energy and Natural Resources

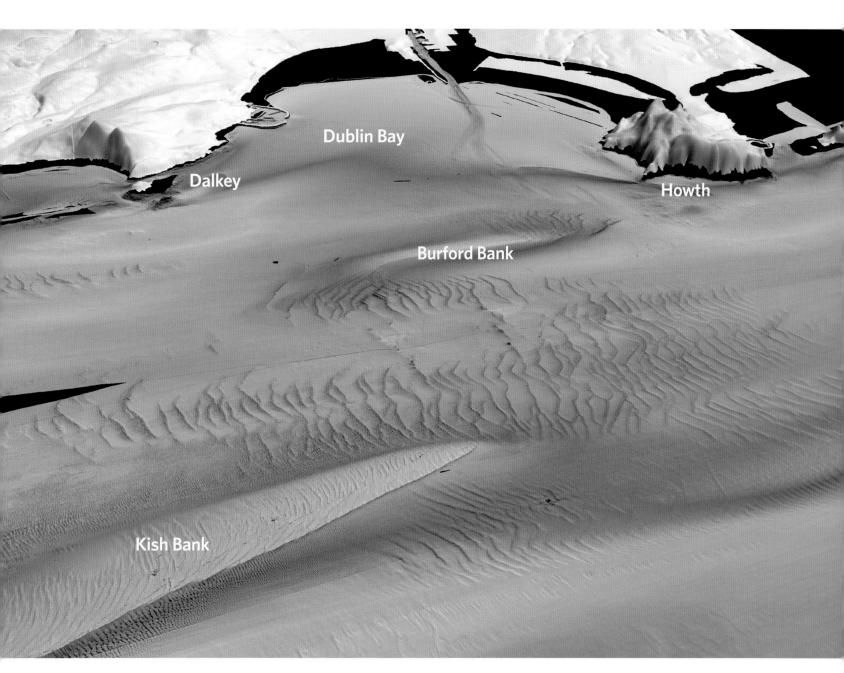

Above: Multibeam view of seabed formations and sand banks off the coast of County Dublin.

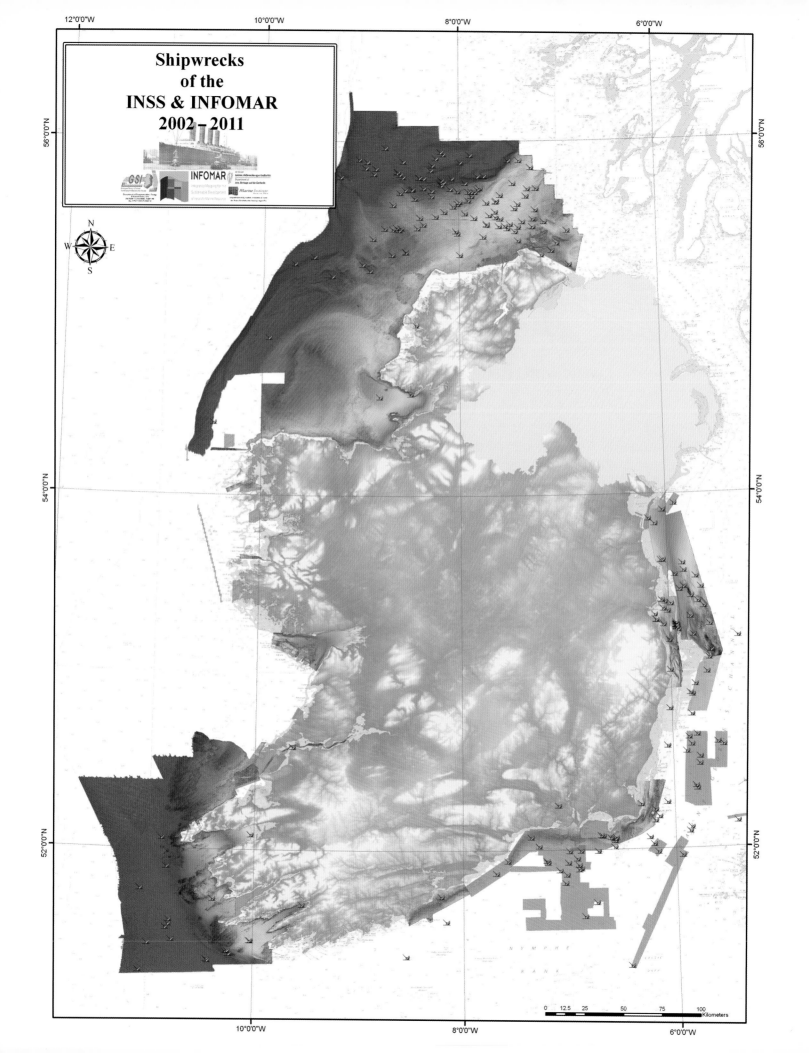

Shipwrecks
of the
INSS & INFOMAR
2002 – 2011

Introduction

For the past 12 years Ireland's offshore waters and coastal seas have been subject to one of the largest seabed surveys in the world, commenced by the Geological Survey of Ireland (GSI) and now being completed as a joint venture with the Marine Institute. To date, along with an earlier government survey, over 540,000km² of seabed have been surveyed, resulting in thousands of seabed features being mapped and investigated, such as coral carbonate mounds, cold-water coral reefs, subsea landslides, fault zones, iceberg scour marks, canyons, reefs and navigational hazards, along with other important geological, biological, heritage and hydrographical features. Equally important are the *c.* 300 shipwrecks that have also been mapped as part of this work. Since 2006 the GSI, in collaboration with the Underwater Archaeology Unit (UAU) of the National Monuments Service, Department of Arts, Heritage and the Gaeltacht, has been carrying out a joint project to research and investigate the shipwrecks that were mapped or discovered during the Irish National Seabed Survey (INSS), conducted between 1999 and 2006, and the INFOMAR project (INtegrated Mapping FOr the

Sustainable Development of Ireland's MArine Resource), underway since 2006. This has resulted in a database of over 300 accurately located shipwrecks, containing detailed information regarding each wreck's condition on the seafloor, its extent, dimensions and water depth, along with a short background history of each vessel and the reason for its loss.

The mapping projects carried out by the INSS and INFOMAR have resulted in the largest systematic survey of the seabed off Ireland, which is of enormous benefit to our marine cultural heritage, particularly by locating and mapping hundreds of wrecks. For the first time, we now have data that provides accurate positioning on numerous

Opposite: A 3D view of Ireland, showing shipwrecks and areas of inshore seabed mapped and surveyed. Approximately 300 wrecks have been discovered, surveyed and mapped to date during the INSS and INFOMAR mapping projects.

Below: The RV *Keary* is named after Raymond Keary, a pioneering marine geologist, and is owned by the GSI. A 15m long, purpose-built, aluminium catamaran, it was designed for surveying shallow waters, with a draft of only 1.7m. It has state-of-the-art hydrographic and geophysical equipment, enabling it to produce survey data to the highest international standards.

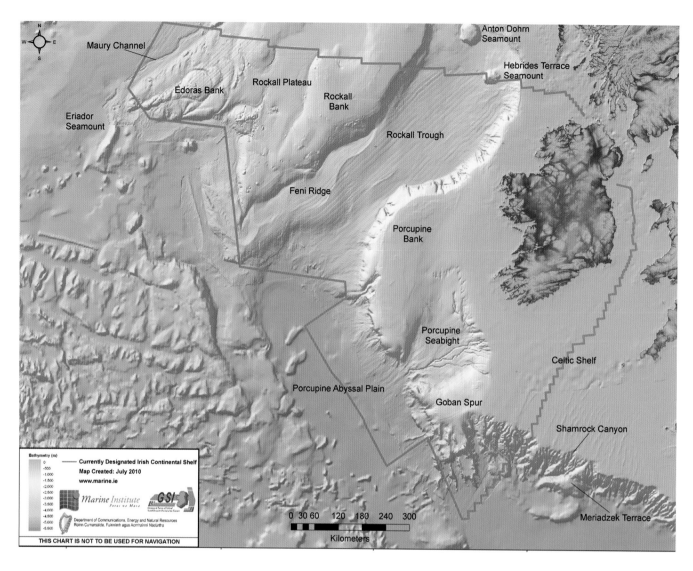

Above: *The Real Map of Ireland* shows the current designated Irish Continental Shelf, one of the largest seabed territories in Europe. The coastal state exercises sovereign rights over the continental shelf for the purpose of exploring and exploiting its natural resources, subject to the provisions in Part VI, UN Convention on the Law of the Sea.

Right: Multibeam image of two iron barges located 6km NE of Skerries, Co. Dublin. The red and yellow indicate higher parts of the wrecks; the blue indicates scouring. They are relatively intact and lie upright in 19m of water. Their identities and when they sank are not known.

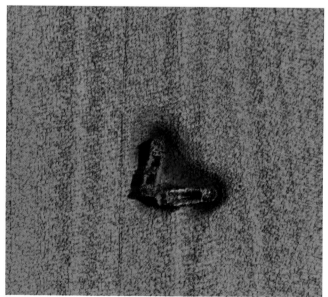

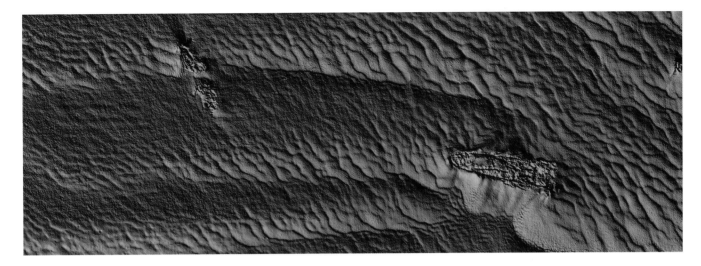

Above: A multibeam image of two wrecks located and surveyed during the INSS and INFOMAR projects. In the centre is the *Bolivar*, a Norwegian cargo vessel that went aground on the Kish Bank in 1947. In the top left is the remains of the 478-ton iron merchant steamer *Vesper*, which was lost on the Kish Bank in 1876.

new wreck sites, along with corrected positions for wrecks previously plotted inaccurately. The INSS mapping projects have also confirmed the locations of many of the more well-known wreck sites around the coast of Ireland. This data enables us to determine the wreck's form, condition, orientation and the seabed morphology surrounding the site. The multibeam data also provides highly accurate information regarding the full extent of a wreck, including its debris zone and associated scour holes, which may also contain wreck material. Information gleaned from seabed surveys increases our understanding of seabed dynamics at wreck sites, thereby contributing to our understanding of wreck site formation processes, wreck site stability and related conservation issues, all of which will contribute to the development of long-term management strategies for this important and fragile element of the cultural resource.

Purpose of this Book

The purpose of this guide to shipwrecks is to highlight Ireland's leading role internationally in seabed and shipwreck mapping, research and heritage management to draw attention to the diverse wealth of resources present on our seabed, particularly the shipwrecks. With this in mind, it was decided to highlight 60 of the most important shipwrecks mapped during the seabed survey mapping projects in an illustrated and accessible format. Each shipwreck is presented as an individual entry, along with its co-ordinates, its water depth and a description of its current condition, plus high-resolution multibeam imagery providing an outline of how the wreck looks on the seafloor. Additionally, the results

of extensive research across a wide range of historical and archaeological sources, carried out by the UAU, are presented as descriptive accounts of each vessel's composition, background, history and ultimate fate. Contemporary photographs, paintings, prints and illustrations are presented for each vessel along with underwater photographs, where available. A number of divers, in particular Ian Lawler, have provided interesting first-hand accounts and detailed descriptions of the current condition of some of the diveable wrecks included in this guide.

The wreck entries are divided into four chapters, listing wrecks chronologically according to date of loss: 3. Historic Wrecks of the 16th, 18th, 19th and early 20th centuries; 4. World War I wrecks; 5. World War II wrecks; 6. Post-war wrecks. As the majority of the wrecks mapped relate to the two World Wars, two introductory chapters are included to provide a context and background, to explain why there were so many wartime losses in the waters off the coast of Ireland. A list of wrecks is presented as an Appendix at the end of the book (*see* p. 176), detailing the positions, dimensions and water depths of all wrecks surveyed thus far by the two mapping projects. It is hoped that this publication will appeal to anyone with a general interest in the maritime history of Ireland and the history of the two World Wars from a maritime perspective. It is also hoped to create awareness amongst the general public, divers, oceanographers, developers, planners and all those who are interested or involved in the management of the marine environment regarding the existence and importance of this fascinating aspect of our maritime heritage.

Following pages: The RMS *Leinster* was attacked and sunk by the German submarine *UB-123*, with the loss of 501 lives. It is remembered as one of the worst tragedies ever to occur in Irish waters. The *Leinster* is one of over 12,000 wrecks listed in the Shipwreck Inventory Database. (Ian Lawler Collection)

1 Work of the INSS and the INFOMAR programme

Charise McKeon

The INFOMAR programme (**IN**tegrated Mapping **FO**r the Sustainable Development of Ireland's **MA**rine **R**esource) is a joint venture between the Geological Survey of Ireland (GSI) and the Marine Institute. The programme succeeded the Irish National Seabed Survey (INSS), which commenced in 1999, ended in 2005 and was one of the largest marine mapping programmes ever undertaken anywhere in the world, with a focus on deep water mapping. Total mapping coverage by the INSS to end 2005 was 432,000 km². Taken together with earlier DCENR (Department of Communications, Energy and Natural Resources) Petroleum Affairs Division mapping, this meant that more than 81% of the Irish designated seabed area (at end 2005) was mapped, to approximately the 200m depth contour. In doing so, the INSS delivered a national asset that has given Ireland a comprehensive dataset to inform and shape present and future economic, environmental, infrastructural, heritage, social and policy issues.

Following the ending of the Survey programme, there remained a crucially important body of work to map commercially valuable inshore and other waters that lay outside the scope of the INSS. Furthermore, a diverse range of navigation, environmental and cultural international legislative obligations also needed to be addressed. The INFOMAR programme, which began in 2006, is intended to address these outstanding issues, while also delivering an enhanced data management and delivery service for data gathered under both the INSS and INFOMAR. This data delivery strategy is intended to promote the creation of value-added products. INFOMAR has focused its efforts on creating a range of integrated mapping products of the physical, chemical and biological features of the seabed in the near-shore area. The programme is funded by the Irish Government through the DCENR, currently as part of the National Development Plan 2007–2013.

The INFOMAR programme utilises a range of vessels from which to undertake geophysical surveying. Primarily, it is the water depth in which work is to take place that governs the choice of vessel. So, for example, deeper bays and areas have been predominantly surveyed by the Marine Institute vessels RV *Celtic Explorer* and RV *Celtic Voyager*. For shallower areas, i.e. less than 20m, the new GSI vessels RV *Geo* and RV *Keary* (named after one of Ireland's pioneering marine geologists, Raymond Keary) are used to carry out the majority of the surveying.

In addition to hydrographic surveying and physical habitat mapping of the seafloor, shipwrecks in Irish waters are one of the many seafloor features mapped in detail under the INFOMAR programme. The majority of shipwrecks found are usually charted named or unnamed wrecks, although some uncharted shipwrecks have also been discovered. The mapping of shipwrecks provides a modern-day inspection of the vessel as it lies on the seafloor, with many resting in their current locations for over 100 years. This information also provides a more accurate position for the location of a shipwreck, which is then used to update the Shipwreck Inventory of Ireland held by the Underwater Archaeology Unit (UAU), Admiralty charts and the database of wrecks produced by the UK Hydrographic Office (UKHO).

Mapping Shipwrecks

The core dataset acquired for both the INSS and the INFOMAR programmes is bathymetric data. Generally, a hull-mounted, Kongsberg Simrad multibeam echosounder (MBES) is used in this acquisition, with additional geophysical equipment also deployed. Various multibeam systems are used, depending on the water depth of the survey environment. The swath width is directly related to the water depth, i.e. the deeper the water, the greater the swath. The EM3002D system, for example, can operate with a swath width up to ten times the water depth, which allows for maximum coverage in a shorter timeframe. Different systems also operate at different frequencies and will therefore have varying numbers of sonar beams within a swath. Systems used throughout the INSS included the

Above: A 3D view of Ireland, from the southwest, showing areas of inshore seabed that have been mapped and surveyed by INFOMAR.

Right: Areas of Ireland's designated waters mapped during the INSS and INFOMAR mapping projects. The darker blue and purple areas are the deepest, indicating depths of over 5km. The red and pink areas are the shallowest, indicating depths of less than 150m.

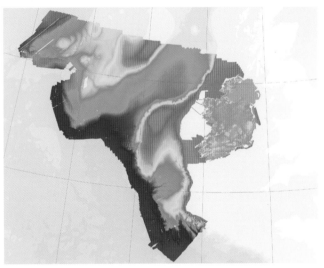

EM120 and the EM1002. The EM3002D MBES is now the main system used in the INFOMAR programme and is one of the highest resolution systems available. During a survey the multibeam data collected is corrected for the following parameters:

- Vessel Position;

- Heading;

- Attitude (heave, pitch and roll);

- Draft value for the echosounder system;

- Sound velocity (corrects for changes in water properties with depth, e.g. salinity and temperature).

Once the data has been collected initial data processing is performed, where further filters are applied to the data. These filters include:

- Total Propagated Error (TPE), which is derived from a combination of the previous parameters; and

- Tide, i.e. data from tide gauges positioned within the survey area to gain an accurate representation of the tide dynamics operating in the area, which improves the accuracy of the depth data.

During acquisition, potential shipwreck targets are checked against the UKHO listing within the survey area. When an object is found that could be a shipwreck, it is resurveyed in accordance with UKHO guidelines, whereby the object is 'boxed in' by running four additional survey lines over it while simultaneously logging water column data. This data is carefully evaluated by the onboard data processor to check if the object is a shipwreck or, as in some cases, some other type of seabed feature, such as a rock outcrop. The majority of shipwrecks surveyed to date were known or charted, but a number of uncharted shipwrecks have also been mapped. Any shipwreck surveyed is reported in detail and this information is sent directly to the UKHO in the form of a hydrographic note. The UKHO will then update the appropriate chart and may issue an immediate notice to mariners if the wreck is deemed a serious navigational hazard. This information is also sent directly to the UAU, for inclusion in the records held there. Additional acoustic mapping systems, such as side-scan sonar and a magnetometer, are also used to further enhance the mapping and imaging of shipwrecks surveyed. In most cases the accuracy of the charted position of the wreck is greatly improved by these means.

As previously mentioned, the shipwrecks mapped by the INSS/INFOMAR have been surveyed using a number of different sonar systems. The specifications of a particular sonar system will ultimately control the quality of the image produced for a shipwreck on the seabed. Throughout the INSS and during the early stages of the INFOMAR programme, multibeam echosounder systems, such as the EM120 and EM1002, were used as the primary means of mapping. These systems were used in accordance with the water depths being surveyed, and the seafloor maps produced ranged between 5m and 75m in resolution. Since 2008 INFOMAR has been predominantly mapping shallower water depths using the EM3002D multibeam echosounder system. This system produces extremely high resolution seafloor mapping images due to its higher operating frequency in shallower water depths. A higher frequency instrument will most often have better resolution and accuracy than a lower frequency instrument for a certain water depth. In accordance with UKHO guidelines, a shipwreck must be surveyed in greater detail within a survey area, i.e. a minimum of four survey lines must be run over the object and the water column data must be logged. It is for this reason that shipwrecks now being mapped under the INFOMAR project can be imaged at resolutions as high as 10cm, in comparison to shipwrecks mapped in deeper waters using lower resolution systems, which average *c.* 1.5–2m in resolution.

Data of the INSS/INFOMAR — Shipwrecks and other features of the seafloor

The INSS and INFOMAR mapping programmes have produced innovative imagery of many different types of seafloor feature, many of which have never been seen in

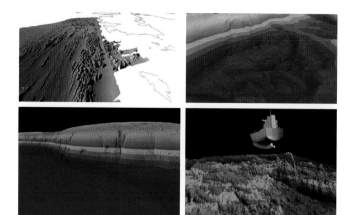

Some of the seafloor features mapped during the INSS and INFOMAR mapping projects.
Clockwise from top left: a deep underwater trench off Ballydavid Head, Co. Kerry; Codling Deep in the Irish Sea; Canyons of the Porcupine Shelf; a shoal mapped in Mannin Bay, Clifden, Co. Galway.

such detail before. These include submarine slides, mound features, deep canyons, ice scour marks, pockmarks, sandbanks and shipwrecks. The multibeam systems used provide a fast and effective means of surveying the bathymetry of the seabed, allowing high-resolution imaging of these features.

To date, the shipwreck database of the INSS/INFOMAR has over 300 entries, providing accurate locations for known and unknown shipwrecks in Irish waters. The presence of a shipwreck in the multibeam data not only allows for the creation of high-resolution images but also provides information on the vessel's dimensions, the depth of water in and around the wreck site and some insight as to how the vessel lies on the seafloor. The INSS/INFOMAR shipwreck database has been developed in three phases.

Since the INSS commenced surveying, in 1999, a dataset of shipwrecks surveyed in multibeam data was compiled by Sean Cullen of the GSI (Phase 1) and this continued to be added to once INFOMAR got underway in 2006. Phase 2 saw an updated shipwreck database as the main output of a joint project between the GSI and the National Monuments Service (NMS), carried out in 2005–6 by Stuart Bennett, Karl Brady and Eibhlín Doyle. The aim of this project was to integrate the shipwreck databases of both organisations into a comprehensive and accurate inventory of shipwrecks in Irish waters. The NMS had been compiling a database of shipwrecks in Irish waters since 1997. The Shipwreck Inventory of Ireland includes all known wrecks for the years up to and including 1945, and approximately 12,000 records have been integrated into the database to date. In addition to combining the two wreck databases by

Tuskar Rock

Wreck

Above: 3D imagery of an unknown shipwreck (lying NE–SW on the seabed) located to the N of Tuskar Rock, off the Wexford coast.

matching the seafloor images and locations from the INSS database with the locations and historical information in the NMS database, a further aim of the joint project was to expand the INSS database. This involved using existing INSS multibeam data to reveal shipwrecks that had previously not been charted, had been inaccurately charted or had not been recorded during a survey. This project saw an addition of 60 shipwrecks to the existing 140 shipwrecks mapped as part of the INSS. The 60 additional shipwrecks were added after re-evaluation of the multibeam data acquired under the INSS. An internal report from this work was produced in 2006 and the project helped to develop a template for the future cataloguing of shipwrecks mapped within the INFOMAR programme.

The third phase of work, leading to this publication, has been carried out under INFOMAR and in addition to the continuation of recording and imaging shipwrecks mapped has also seen the establishment of a working partnership between the GSI and the Underwater Archaeology Unit, NMS. A series of shipwreck information sheets are produced annually and these contain a combination of information for a particular shipwreck from INFOMAR

multibeam data and NMS archaeological records. These shipwreck information sheets are available to download from www.infomar.ie. Furthermore, 2011 saw a successful joint survey and excavation of a possible Spanish Armada wreck at Rutland Island, Co. Donegal.

Future of INFOMAR

The next phase of the INFOMAR programme aims to build on national marine expertise to promote and encourage research in marine science and to spread this expertise across government agencies, third-level institutions and a strengthened private sector. Overall, it is expected that the programme outputs will contribute to and enhance Ireland's international status as a leader in seabed-mapping techniques. It is also hoped that datasets such as the Shipwreck Inventory and the INSS/INFOMAR shipwreck database will be integrated into different sectors, such as marine tourism. It is envisaged that further collaborative work on surveying significant shipwreck sites of archaeological importance can be carried out between INFOMAR and the UAU. Such collaboration will highlight further the need to protect underwater archaeology sites, through the work of the Underwater Archaeology Unit of the National Monuments Service.

2 The Underwater Archaeology Unit and the Protection of Ireland's Shipwrecks

Karl Brady and Fionnbarr Moore

Why protect shipwrecks?

The maritime heritage of Ireland is rich and wide-ranging and is intrinsic to the national identity, both past and present. This aspect of the country's heritage is cultural and natural, being widely reflected in the coastal landscape, seascapes, wildlife, ecology, customs, folklore, folklife, history, architecture, archaeological sites and traditional boats of Ireland. Shipwrecks form an integral part of the maritime heritage and can provide important links to the story of our past, giving us unique insights into major historical events, such as the Spanish Armada and the two World Wars. Our maritime history would be incomplete without the stories of the numerous vernacular craft, local fishing boats and coastal traders that sank over the centuries, often resulting in loss of life. Such losses have caused immense hardship and heartache for coastal communities the length and breadth of the island, and it is important that the human tragedy associated with the wrecks listed in this book should not be forgotten.

Shipwrecks can be like time capsules, containing fascinating information relating to a particular event or period, but they can also help us to appreciate the dynamics at play in our coastal waters over the millennia and can add significantly to how we map and interpret the country's history. Shipwrecks are the best illustration of the fact that events in Ireland rarely took place in isolation from the wider world. The evidence for trade with other countries and the exploitation of local maritime resources is tangibly present in the accounts of recorded wrecks and in the physical evidence that survives at wreck sites. In addition, the stories of these shipwrecks reflect evidence for war, conflict, invasion and the cultural exchange of ideas through the centuries. In spite of this, the significance of the maritime seagoing and seaborne heritage is often overlooked in general accounts of Ireland's history and archaeology. This is because many people consider shipwrecks to be inaccessible, the sole preserve of divers, oceanographers and maritime archaeologists. This is not the case, however. As sources of information on our heritage, shipwrecks belong to us all. It is hoped that by highlighting some of the more important shipwrecks in Irish waters in this user-friendly book, it will promote a much wider awareness and appreciation of their significance and their value in helping us to understand the development of Ireland's heritage.

The Shipwreck Inventory of Ireland

Ireland has a vast marine resource: the coastline is more than 7,000km long, while the country's designated waters encompass more than 900,000km² of seabed, which is ten times that of its landmass. Since 1997 the National Monuments Service (within the Department of Arts, Heritage and the Gaeltacht) has been endeavouring to quantify and manage the archaeological resource in the waters off our coast. As part of that process the NMS set up an Underwater Archaeology Unit (UAU) to deal specifically with this area. Thus the role of the UAU within the National Monuments Service is to manage and protect the underwater cultural heritage.

The UAU has a threefold approach to the management and protection of the underwater resource: I. compiling a comprehensive inventory of shipwrecks; II. assessing marine planning referrals; and III. ground-truthing/surveying/excavating newly discovered or vulnerable wrecks or other underwater sites. In order to fulfil the Department's statutory obligations under the National Monuments Acts 1930–2004, the UAU is in the process of compiling a comprehensive dataset of underwater archaeology sites around the coast, which will be used as a management tool for addressing planning and development impacts, licensing dives and activities on protected wreck sites and carrying out monument protection duties related to the underwater cultural heritage.

The primary element of this dataset is the Shipwreck Inventory of Ireland, which contains a comprehensive

Above: A UAU archaeologist recording a large wheel from a siege-gun carriage carried on the Spanish Armada vessel *La Trinidad Valencera*, which was lost on 16 September 1588 in Kinnagoe Bay, Co. Donegal. The wreck was first discovered in 1971. From 2004 to 2006 the UAU undertook a detailed survey and investigation of the wreck. (Photo Connie Kelleher)

Right: During the 19th century the British parliament established a 'Select committee appointed to inquire into the causes of Shipwrecks' and from 1856 onwards annual reports were produced. This map from the 1866 Report illustrates the number and general location of vessels stranded and wrecked in the Irish Sea in the preceding year. (Courtesy of the National Library of Ireland)

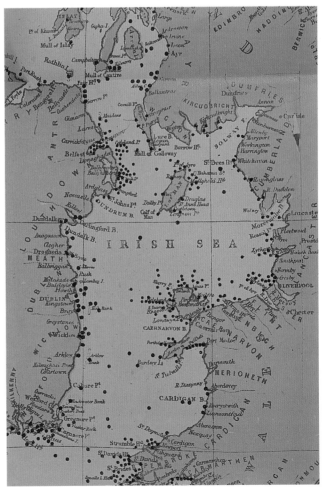

database of all recorded wrecks in Irish territorial waters and in the designated area of the Continental Shelf. The Inventory is largely a desk-based study, gleaned from a variety of documentary sources. It is planned to publish four volumes in the coming years, detailing the full findings of the Inventory. In 2008 the first volume of the Inventory was published, covering the eastern counties of Louth, Meath, Dublin and Wicklow. *Shipwreck Inventory of Ireland: Louth, Meath, Dublin and Wicklow* is published by The Stationery Office and available for purchase through the Government Publications Sales Office, Sun Alliance House, Molesworth Street, Dublin 2, or from any bookseller.)

Alongside, and complementing, the Shipwreck Inventory, the UAU has been compiling a location map of all shipwreck sites on the Continental Shelf/EEZ (Exclusive Economic Zone) of Ireland for which there is a reported location (*see* p. 12). The UAU maintains a database of over 12,000 wrecks, and of these 25% have recorded positions. The location map is a work in

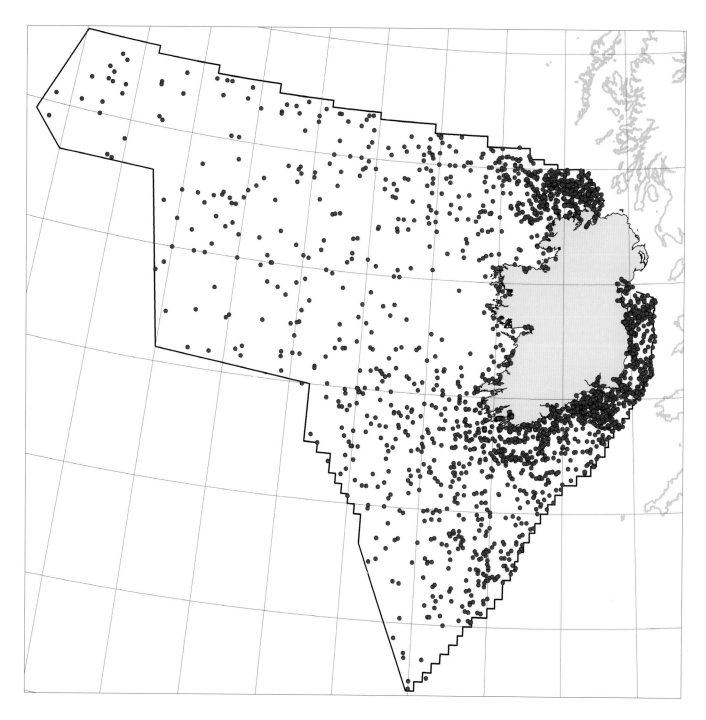

progress, but it represents the most up-to-date information on known wreck locations for the area in question; it will be subject to revision as research continues. The map information is derived from a wide variety of sources, including UKHO wreck data, 18th- and 19th-century surveys and sea charts, Lloyd's List and Lloyd's Register of Shipping, Parliamentary Papers, local and international journals, various websites, fishermen's marks and charts, divers' reports and, of course, data collected during the INSS and the INFOMAR programme.

The sports diving and technical-diving communities have played, and continue to play, a key role in the discovery of new wreck sites, as well as researching and surveying previously known sites. This reflects a growing

Above: An archaeologist investigates two iron cannon from a 17th-century wreck in Broadhaven Bay, Co. Mayo. The wreck lies in shallow water and 12 cannon have been located to date by the UAU. The identity of the vessel has yet to be confirmed, but available evidence suggests it is the remains of a Dutch East Indiaman merchant vessel. (Photo Karl Brady)

awareness amongst all users of the sea and waterways of the fragile nature of underwater archaeological sites and the need to protect them. Various divers and diving clubs have participated in the discovery of and research on numerous wrecks, including many of the wrecks featured in this book. It is hoped that future co-operation with all interested parties will ensure the long-term preservation of these sites for generations to come.

Further research, survey work and information gained from divers, fishermen, coastal users and archaeologists will continue to add to the shipwreck archive, with entries being updated, where necessary. The Shipwreck Inventory of Ireland Archive is available for consultation, by prior arrangement, in the offices of the Underwater Archaeology Unit, National Monuments Service, Department of Arts, Heritage and the Gaeltacht, Custom House, Dublin 1. It is also planned to make the detailed interactive shipwreck maps available on the Department's website (www.archaeology.ie) in the coming years.

The Shipwrecks

Given the high levels of maritime activity off the Irish coast over the centuries, it is not surprising that there are over 12,000 recorded wrecks in Irish waters. This figure, which is revised regularly, is considered to represent only a fraction of the real number of wrecks in our waters; it is estimated that the true number could be as high as 30,000. Far from being dead history, these wrecks tell a compelling story of power, greed, politics and religion, providing a colourful insight into the country's history. It is clear that boats and ships played a vital role in the settlement and development of the island. The wrecks featured here are associated not only with important Irish historical events but with major international events as well, such as the Spanish Armada campaign of 1588, the failed French invasion attempt in 1796 and, in particular, World War I and World War II. These wrecks, and those yet to be discovered, are repositories of important and enlightening information, which makes their preservation and examination so essential.

A wide range of vessel types is represented in the database, reflecting over 400 years of seafaring and including wooden sail ships, barques, barges, fishing vessels, paddle steamships, submarines, warships and ocean-going liners. Of the 300 wrecks mapped to date during the seabed surveys, only ten predate World War I: one wreck dates to the 16th century and one to the 18th century, while eight wrecks date to the 19th century. Of the rest, 35 date to World War I, 53 to World War II and 33 to the latter half of the 20th century. In all, 129 wrecks in the database have yet to be identified, although most of these are likely to date to the two major World War conflicts of the 20th century.

The oldest wreck included in the book was mapped as part of the underwater archaeological excavation of a late 16th-century wreck off Rutland Island, Co. Donegal, carried out by the UAU (*see* p. 26). The site, and the seabed area in general, was surveyed by the GSI using the RV *Keary* and RV *Geo*, successfully illustrating the usefulness of multibeam in mapping older, wooden wreck sites whose profiles are normally difficult to identify and interpret on the seabed. It is too early to say at this stage what the original identity of the vessel was, but it is possible that this wreck was one of 26 Spanish vessels lost off the Irish coast during the failed invasion attempt of England by King Phillip II in 1588.

The remains of up to ten, most likely 19th-century, wooden wrecks have also been identified and surveyed on the Kish Bank, off the coast of Dublin. The most notable of these is probably the wreck of the *Sir Charles Napier* (*see* p. 33), which was lost en route from Liverpool to Sierra Leone, carrying a cargo of iron pots and hoops. The outline of the wreck is clearly visible in the multibeam data along with part of the cargo, still in its original position. Even more impressive still is the multibeam data of the *Manchester Merchant*, originally a Boer War transport, which was lost in Dingle Bay in 1903, en route

Above: A UAU archaeologist recording two cannon on an early 17th-century wreck site located in Dunworley Bay, Co. Cork. (Photo Connie Kelleher)

from New Orleans to Manchester with a cargo of cotton. The internal holds of the ship are clearly visible along with the vessel's boilers, which stand over 5m high above the seabed, abaft of amidships. The construction make-up of the ship can be discerned, with hull plating visible scattered on the seabed to either side of the wreck.

The numerous shipwrecks that lie strewn on the seabed to the north and south of Ireland are testimony to the great maritime conflict that was played out in Irish waters during World War I. Lying astride the western approaches to Britain, the waters off the north and south of Ireland were of such strategic interest to the 'belligerent' European powers that the German Navy, the *Kaiserliche Marine*, orchestrated a deadly submarine offensive there, resulting in these waters becoming known as 'killing lanes'. The protection enjoyed by Allied maritime traffic by virtue of travelling in the broad expanse of the Atlantic was lost as soon as it entered the narrowing approaches to the north and south of Ireland. This is borne out in the estimate that there are at least 1,800 shipwrecks in the waters surrounding Ireland, all casualties of that terrible conflict.

The most famous loss during World War I was that of the Cunard-owned *Lusitania* (*see* p. 61). At the time, the *Lusitania* was one of the largest liners plying the transatlantic route. Its size offered no protection, however, when it was torpedoed in May 1915 by the German submarine *U-20* off the Old Head of Kinsale, Co. Cork, resulting in the loss of 1,198 civilian lives. The sinking of the *Lusitania*, along with other neutral American ships, was thought to be a critical catalyst in America's decision to enter the war in 1917. The wreck of the grand liner lies in 100m of water, approximately 22km south of the Old Head of Kinsale, and is inaccessible to all but the most experienced divers. It was one of the first wrecks to be surveyed during the INSS and the multibeam imagery of the wreck shows the once majestic liner languishing in a collapsed state, with a large area of debris lying to starboard of the wreck. It serves as a sad reminder of the vagaries of warfare.

Another notable loss, considered one of the worst maritime tragedies ever to take place in Irish waters, was the sinking of the RMS *Leinster* (*see* p. 111). The steamer had survived several close encounters with German submarines throughout World War I, but with just weeks to go before the war ended, the *Leinster*'s luck ran out. On 10 October 1918, 5 miles east of the Kish Light Vessel and en route to Holyhead, the RMS *Leinster* was torpedoed and sunk by a German submarine, with the loss of 501 lives. The multibeam imagery shows the badly damaged wreck lying partially buried in sand, almost wedged in between two large sandwaves.

As in World War I, during World War II German U-boats patrolled the Atlantic approaches to the north and south of Ireland, attacking merchant ships in an attempt to cut off Britain's vital supply of food, oil, weapons and raw materials, in a drawn-out struggle that became known as the Battle of the Atlantic. Within hours of the outbreak of war the passenger liner *Athenia* (*see* p. 76) was torpedoed some 250 miles west of Inishtrahull, Co. Donegal. The *Athenia* was en route from Glasgow to Montreal, carrying 315 crew and 1,103 passengers. It was torpedoed by *U-30*, which mistook the liner for an armed merchant cruiser; 123 lives were lost. The exact location of the wreck of the *Athenia* was unknown until it was surveyed during the INSS because it lies in about 190m of water on the Rockall Bank. The depth of water makes it difficult to gain high-resolution multibeam imagery of the wreck, but it was possible to finally chart its exact location on the seabed.

While the number of vessels lost off Ireland's coasts during World War II is significantly lower than in World War I, there are still estimated to be 700 war wrecks in the waters around Ireland. The largest single casualty of the war was the 42,000-ton *Empress of Britain* (*see* p. 137), which was bombed by a German long-range Focke-Wulf 200 Condor airplane on 26 October, when it was en route from Cape Town to Liverpool. The *Empress* burned fiercely for three days, and finally sank on 28 October after being hit by a torpedo fired by *U-32*. The wreck, which lies in a water depth of 160m, 90km WNW of Bloody Foreland, Co. Donegal, was surveyed in 2007 and the multibeam imagery indicates that it is lying upside-down on a flat seabed. Alongside these striking examples, many other high-profile shipwrecks were surveyed during the INSS and the INFOMAR mapping projects and some of the more interesting stories relating to these are presented in Chapters 4 and 5.

Now that the survey data for each wreck has been analysed in relation to vessel dimensions, shape and form, in tandem with historical information, UKHO data and divers' reports, over 55% of the 300 wrecks mapped thus far have been identified. It is hoped that future survey work, research and collaboration with divers, fishermen and boatmen will lead to the successful identification of the remaining wrecks. In this regard, the NMS (www.archaeology.ie) and the GSI (www.infomar.ie) would be very interested to hear from divers who may be able to provide additional details on wrecks listed in the shipwreck database or locations for wrecks not listed in the database.

Legislation and the Protection of Shipwrecks

There is strong legislation in place to protect historic wrecks in Ireland's waters. The primary piece of legislation in this regard is the National Monuments (Amendment) Act 1987, which affords protection to all wrecks over 100 years old within Ireland's designated waters and to all archaeological objects underwater. Wrecks less than 100 years old can also be protected, if considered to be of particular historic importance. The wreck of RMS *Lusitania* is the first shipwreck of less than 100 years old to be protected under the relevant provisions of the Act. Under the Merchant Shipping (Salvage & Wreck) Act 1993, in the absence of a known owner the Director of the National Museum of Ireland can claim salvaged wreck material on behalf of the State. Under the National Monuments (Amendment) Act 1987 licences are required in order to undertake diving, excavation and metal-detection at protected wreck sites or at the site of an archaeological object. Finders of a wreck (over 100 years old) or an archaeological object underwater are obliged to report such discoveries to the Director of the National Museum of Ireland in the case of objects, or to the Minister for Arts, Heritage and the Gaeltacht in the case of a wreck. Dive licence application forms can be downloaded from www.archaeology.ie or by requesting an application form from the Licensing Section, National Monuments Service, Custom House, Dublin 1.

Following pages: An *Illustrated London News* engraving showing the loss of the *Neptune* during the great storm of 9 February 1861. It was one of 40 vessels stranded and wrecked in and around Dún Laoghaire Harbour on that dreadful night. (Courtesy of the National Library of Ireland)

3 Shipwrecks of the Modern Historic Period, c.1580–c.1914

Connie Kelleher, Karl Brady and Fionnbarr Moore

The dangers of the Irish coast to shipping were well known from the earliest of times but no more so than during the 16th century, when the ragged remains of the once mighty Spanish Armada fleet were making the return trip to Spain, following their catastrophic attempt to invade England. Defeated through a combination of English naval ingenuity in the Channel and horrific weather conditions in the North Sea and around the west coast of Ireland, the duke of Medina Sedonia issued a warning to the commanders of all his ships:

'take great heed lest you fall upon the Island of Ireland for fear of the harm that may happen unto you upon that coast.'

His astute warning was sounded in vain. Of the 130-strong fleet of ships that had set sail from Lisbon on 28 May 1588, only half made it back home again. Thirty-nine vessels were captured or lost, while 26 were wrecked off the Irish coastline in September and October of that year.

The fate of the ships of the Spanish Armada is perhaps one of the best-known accounts of ship losses off Ireland's coast. However, during the modern historic period the number of ship losses began to rise. This increase was the result of advances in ship-building capacity and related technology, as well as the growth of international and transatlantic trade. The establishment of coastal communities across the world to take advantage of the growing global trading routes and an increase in fish stocks in Irish waters led to an increase in shipwrecks and related incidents. Many of the ships involved in transatlantic voyages did not complete their journeys and had the misfortune of being cast ashore on the coast of Ireland.

This is well illustrated by the loss of ships like the *Emanuel* in Smerwick Harbour, in September 1578. The *Emanuel* was part of Martin Frobisher's final expedition, which attempted to find a navigable route through the Northwest Passage and on to the Far East. However, on its return journey from Baffin Island to London, the storm-battered ship, which was laden with a cargo thought to be gold ore, was driven into Smerwick harbour and wrecked near Dún an Óir, or the Fort of Gold (so named after the *Emanuel*'s cargo). Once the rest of Frobisher's fleet returned to London, it soon became apparent that the cargo of ore had very little actual gold content and therefore was deemed worthless.

Thankfully, the recording of such wrecking events subsequently became more systematic and this has added incrementally to our shipwreck records. The study of such shipwrecks provides us with first-hand evidence for ship typology, for trade with other parts of the world and for the exploitation of local maritime resources. Furthermore, evidence for conflict and war can be also gleaned through the study of artefactual assemblages on these wreck sites, as can information on invasion and the cultural exchange of ideas through the centuries. By assessing and mapping these wrecks it becomes evident that the geographical location of the island of Ireland, adjacent to Britain and centred on the North Atlantic sea lanes between Europe and the wider world, is not on the periphery as might be presumed. The study of wrecks shows that Ireland was of such strategic value that events on and around the island rarely took place in isolation, but invariably were connected to developments as they unfolded across the globe.

The expansion of trading routes during this period, combined with ongoing competition for maritime supremacy between the main European powers, meant there was a definite increase in the volume of shipping movements on the Atlantic fringes of Europe. The coastal waters of Ireland, particularly around the eastern and southern coastline, consequently saw large numbers of ships lost through a variety of forces, both natural and man-made. With advancements in ship-building technology from the mid-16th century onwards, larger, faster and more heavily armed ships plied the waters of the world. Oared

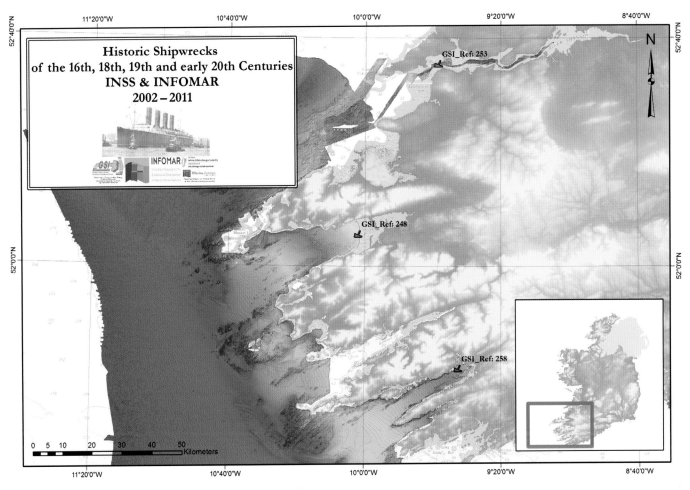

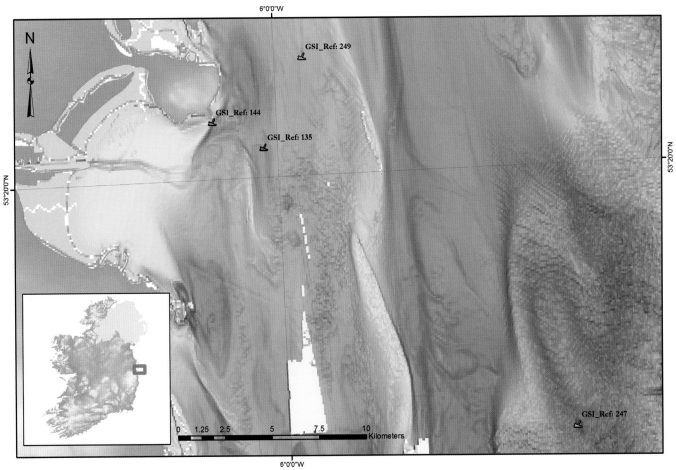

Legend

VESSEL TYPE ⚓ BATTLESHIP ⚓ CARGO VESSEL ⚓ GUN FRIGATE ⚓ PADDLE TUG ⚓ PASSENGER SHIP ⚓ STEAM COASTER ⚓ STEAM COLLIER

Above: A contemporary depiction of the Spanish Armada engaging with the English fleet in the English Channel in August 1588. Of the 130 ships that had set sail from Spain, only half made the return journey. In all, 26 were wrecked off the Irish coastline during September and October 1588. (Courtesy of the National Maritime Museum, Greenwich)

galleys gave way to stately galleons, while carracks and caravels were replaced by fluyts, barques and brigantines. Shipyards in London and on the east coast of Britain became major centres of production for these new designs and timber from Irish forests was exploited to provide the raw material for this exponential growth in production.

Ship travel knew few boundaries and new places began to be explored: colonial merchant adventurers sought out fresh business prospects in distant lands and speculative settlers boarded ships in the Old World with their sights set on the New. These ships left the ports and harbours of mainland Europe, Britain and, to a degree Ireland, and many of them used the ports and harbours of Ireland as stopovers on their outward or homeward journeys. When homeward bound many of these ships, such as the large, fully armed merchantmen of the Dutch, Danish and English East Indies companies, would have been laden down with expensive and exotic goods from far-flung places. Naturally, this meant they presented rich pickings for pirates and privateers, as well as welcome windfalls for wreckers. For their owners, on the other hand, their loss would have spelt economic disaster. A number of these great merchantmen are recorded as having been lost off the coast of Ireland, but to date only scant evidence for them has been identified. The 400-ton English East Indiaman, *Henry*, is one such vessel that came to grief off the Irish coast in July 1685, the remains of which have yet to be identified. Having made most of the arduous journey from the Far East, this 20-gun ship was seeking shelter in Ventry harbour, Co. Kerry, when it was attacked and boarded by 100 men from a 20-gun French privateer. During the ensuing engagements, the *Henry* caught fire and was driven ashore. Seventy of the French privateers lost their lives in the engagement compared to only a small number of the East Indiaman's crew. Even though the vessel burnt to the middle deck, the cargo was later salvaged.

This increase in shipping activity in Irish waters – resulting from factors such as the intensification of the fishing industry, ships stopping over en route to the New World and the growth in trade, both local and between Ireland and the wider world – naturally resulted in an increase in the number of vessels being wrecked off the Irish coast during the 17th century. However, less than 2% of wrecks recorded in the Shipwreck Inventory of Ireland date to the period, highlighting the lack of importance the authorities at the time placed on recording such incidents. Where records do survive, they are very often vague or refer to important naval engagements, bad storms where many ships were lost, the drowning of an important ruler or ecclesiastical figure while voyaging at sea, or to a valuable cargo having been lost. The sinking of the *Laurell*, in Kenmare Bay in January 1693, is a good example of this. The *Laurell* was a 150-ton ship driven ashore en route from Jamaica to London with a cargo of indigo, ginger, cotton, logwood, Roman vitriol, sugar, pieces of eight and £2,500 worth of gold wedges. The locals attempted to pillage the ship's lucrative cargo, but were prevented by local customs officials. The cargo was later salvaged by the customs authorities.

On the home front, Ireland was experiencing great changes during this period. Following the fall of the old Gaelic order in the latter part of the 16th century and the colonisation of Irish lands in tandem with the mass transportation of native Irish to the plantations of Jamaica and the Caribbean during the 17th century, ships played a central, if conflicted, role in Ireland's transition to full English rule. In the middle of the 17th century, when Ireland was embroiled in rebellions as part of the Wars of the Three Kingdoms (1639–53), Cromwell's navy attempted to control the ports and harbours, but was met with resolute force by the privateers of the Irish Confederate fleet. A wreck recently discovered on the Duncannon Bar, Waterford harbour, may be the remains of the *Great Lewis*, the Parliamentary flagship, and provides a tangible link to this period of intensive maritime conflict. This was a time when the Irish Confederates inflicted losses on Cromwell's navy and the war on land was being strongly influenced by the war at sea.

Constant throughout these two centuries were the pirate ships and fleets that targeted merchant vessels and were themselves lost in remote coves and havens in Ireland. There

Above: A diver investigates a bronze *sacre* on the wreck of the *Juliana* in 1985, one of three Spanish Armada transports wrecked off Streedagh, Co. Sligo, during a gale on 21 September 1588. The *Santa Maria de la Visón* and *La Lavia* were also wrecked during the same storm, which resulted in the loss of over 1,000 lives. (Photo Susan Balfe)

is a tradition in west Cork that one such pirate ship, an Algerian rover, was lost in Dunworley Bay. The ship formed part of the pirate fleet from the Barbary Coast, which took part in the infamous 'Sack of Baltimore'. The raid on the coastal village of Baltimore took place in June 1631, and up to 109 English villagers, predominantly settlers, were captured and sold into a life of slavery in Algiers.

As a result of continued colonial expansion into the New World, Africa and Asia, navies were being continually developed and streamlined. By the close of the 17th century the French and English naval forces were comparative in size and strength. European powers looked to take the lead in ocean dominance through amphibious expeditions and outright war. A series of water-based battles decided the outcome of power struggles in this period, including the Anglo-Dutch wars of the second half of the 17th century (c. 1652–74) and the Danish-Swedish Wars (1643–5). From an Irish perspective, however, the Battle of Bantry Bay in 1689 was the greatest naval battle fought in home waters in terms of numbers of ships and troops. The French intended landing some 1,500 troops in Bantry, but were intercepted by the English navy. There followed a four-hour sea battle, with ship damage and troop losses on both sides. Such hard-fought coastal engagements would become a recurrent theme during the next century.

As the 17th century drew to a close and the 18th century dawned, Ireland experienced slow but significant development of its seaport towns and harbours, following the plantation policies of the English crown. Ship design began to follow established lines and from the middle of the century onwards many of the key towns on the eastern seaboard of Ireland became centres not only of

Above: The Battle of Bantry Bay in 1689 was the greatest naval battle ever fought in Irish waters. This painting depicts English and French ships in fierce battle, however it is unclear if the painting portrays the Battle of Bantry or another naval engagement of the time. Artist: Adriaen van Diest or Willem van de Velde the Younger. (Courtesy of the National Maritime Museum, Greenwich)

shipbuilding but of ship owning. Although the opening decades of that century saw a decline in exports due to depleted fish stocks around the coast and a series of bad harvests, this picked up again and trade increased between the eastern ports and those in England and Wales. In particular, the ports of Bristol and later Liverpool became centres of intense merchant activity, with a consequential increase in shipping across the Irish Sea, which inevitably led to more incidents of shipwreck. Throughout this period certain ships carrying a specific cargo would have plied this stretch of water, using the Channel and Irish Sea and calling at Irish ports to restock with victuals or to take refuge from bad weather. These were the slave ships of companies like the Royal African Company or the South Sea Company, and wreck data from remote bays, like that of Dunworley in County Cork, where the slave trader *Amity* was lost in 1700, attest to this horrific trade in human cargo and the often almost casual loss of life of these helpless prisoners.

As a direct result of this increase in shipping, advances continued apace in the areas of navigation, lighthouse building, mail transport and delivery by sea. While this

did improve conditions for seafarers, it could not prevent all ship loss. Politically, by the close of the 18th century several restrictions on trade had been lifted through lobbying by the now free parliament in Dublin, and as a result exports to the Continent began to increase again. Nonetheless, there was still resentment and frustration within the Irish political fraternity and this culminated in another attempted landing of French troops in Bantry Bay in 1796, with consequential loss of ships due to storms and ill-conceived plans. The French Frigate *La Surveillante* (*see* p.28), which was scuttled in Bantry Bay in January 1797, was part of this fleet, as was *l'Impatiente*, which sank off Mizen Head, Co. Cork, in late December 1796. This was one of the opening acts in the series of attacks and counterattacks that eventually led to the 1798 Rebellion, bringing Ireland into the Napoleonic Wars (1803–15). Once again, Ireland's strategic position in the North Atlantic was evident, with the control of ports and harbours and, in particular, its naval bases seen as critical by the English authorities, who feared Ireland would be used as a 'back door' to invade Britain. Cork became one of the main naval ports on the southern coast and eventually, during the course of the following century, developed into one of Britain's primary global naval bases. Up until now the recording of shipwrecks had been sporadic at best, with very little information transcribed. That changed from the middle of the 18th century, when the systematic recording of ship losses began. This has

Above: Early 20th-century postcard produced by the Ellerman Lines to promote their 'City Line' service to India. The postcard illustrates the gradual transition of sail-powered vessels to steam-powered vessels during the late 19th and early 20th centuries. (Ian Lawler Collection)

provided us with comprehensive records from around the Irish coast from this point onwards.

During the 19th century the Irish Sea became one of the busiest waterways in the world. Ireland forged greater trading links with Britain, but mass emigration on foot of the devastating Great Famine (1845–52) meant that the ports, harbours and seaways around Ireland saw unprecedented maritime traffic. Ship types changed as steamships and passenger liners began to open the way for an increase in passenger traffic across the Atlantic or from the western ports of Britain, travelling down the Irish coast on the way to America and Australia. The two most prominent shipping companies, the White Star Line and the Cunard Line, began to build large ocean-going cruise ships to ferry passengers from all walks of life across the seas, buoyed by the hope of a new life in far off lands. Composite warships began to be built, too, made of iron and wood, and warfare at sea took on greater dimensions with developments in armament, communications and naval tactics.

The sheer volume of shipping now plying the waters around Ireland, involved in trade, migration and naval patrols, resulted in an enormous number of vessels being wrecked on her unforgiving coast during the 19th century. That century has, without doubt, the highest number of

wrecks recorded for any period in Irish history: it is estimated that up to 60% of all wrecks in Irish waters date to this time. A closer look at the statistics indicates the magnitude of the number of vessels being lost at the time: in 1852, 102 vessels were lost off the Irish coast; in 1855, 127 vessels were lost; while in 1856, 155 were lost. This averages about one wreck every three days. The impact of this devastating statistic must have been felt the length and breadth of the country, both in terms of loss of life and significant economic impacts. The wrecking of the City of Dublin Steam Packet Company's paddle steamer, the *Queen Victoria*, off the Baily Lighthouse at Howth in 1853, with the loss of 80 lives and its valuable cargo, provides a grim illustration of the impact of even one such loss (*see* p.31). Equally, one of the worst storm events ever recorded off the Irish coast occurred in 1861, resulting in the loss of dozens of ships and numerous lives. The figures for ship losses remain relatively similar up to the start of World War I. Surveys by INFOMAR have identified many 19th-century wrecks, while a recent survey of the Kish Bank has mapped and surveyed at least ten wrecks from this period, including the wreck of the *Sir Charles Napier* (*see* p.32), which was lost en route from Liverpool to Sierra Leone, carrying a cargo of iron pots and hoops, and the wreck of the *Glenorchy* (*see* p.33), a Glasgow-registered, 1,285-ton iron merchant sailing ship that was lost en route to Bombay with coal, railway sleepers and railway machinery.

The second half of the 19th century saw the gradual replacement of the older sailing ships by clippers and steamers on the long-haul voyages across the Atlantic and on the trading routes between Ireland, Britain and mainland Europe. This period saw the emergence of iron-clad battle ships as the vessel of choice for the major navies around the world, while paddle steamers moved across seas and up rivers, bringing great improvements to the speed and efficiency of water-borne trade. The opening of the Suez Canal in 1869 cut over 4,000 miles off the journey to India and made trade with the East and Australia easier and safer.

A good example of the newly developed iron-clad battleship is the HMS *Vanguard* (*see* p.34), recently surveyed by the Seabed Survey, which was lost on the Kish Bank in 1875 following a collision with its sister ship, HMS *Iron Duke*. Some of the wider trading connections and the range of vessel types are also reflected in wrecks featured here, such as the *Vesper* (*see* p.36), an iron steamship bringing coal and sugar from Glasgow to Dunkirk and lost on the Kish Bank, and the SS *Premier* (*see* p.38), a cargo

Below: The *Carnarvonshire*, a 1,274-ton barque, was typical of the vessels plying the waters between England, Ireland, Europe and America at this time. However, its luck ran out when it went ashore at Yokane Point, Co. Cork, in April 1896. It soon afterwards capsized and sank in deeper water, but the 21 crew made it ashore safely. (Ian Lawler Collection)

steamship en route from Hamburg to Limerick that went down in the Shannon Estuary in 1898 following a collision with the paddle steamer *Mermaid* of Waterford.

Following the American Civil War (1861–5) the American merchant fleet went into decline, but trade with the USA continued to increase and some of the wrecks featured in this volume – such as the *Manchester Merchant* (*see* p.40) with its cargo of 13,000 bales of cotton bound for the cotton mills of Lancashire in 1903, only to end up a ball of flame off the west coast of Ireland – are indicative of the continuing importance of this trade. By 1870 the voyage to America from Europe had been cut to two weeks and by 1890, with the development of the Atlantic liner and the accompanying technological progress, the journey was down to six days. Ireland played a key role in the development of faster and more luxurious liners, and the Harland and Wolff shipyard in Belfast produced a number of the world's largest liners in the early years of the 20th century, including the *Celtic* in 1901, which ran aground and was wrecked outside Cork harbour in 1928, and the ill-fated *Titanic* in 1912. Other ports in Ireland served as centres of ship-building in this period and in the 19th century. Waterford, for example, was a major centre of production, building five transatlantic liners amongst a range of other vessels.

Shipyards, like the Tyrell family yard in Arklow, are representative of ongoing boat building on a smaller scale and reflect the long tradition of innovative boat building around the Irish coast. By the early 20th century schooners were giving way to steam-powered trawlers in the fishing grounds of Europe and on the east coast of the USA and Canada, leading to larger catches and significant expansion in the fishing industry.

The close of the 19th century also saw Europe emerging from a period of great uncertainty into one of relative prosperity and calm. Following the Franco-Prussian war (1870–71), German unification was achieved under Otto von Bismarck and Europe enjoyed peace for the next 30 years. Germany took a greater interest in the Atlantic trade route and developed its own fleet of liners. Italian unification had also been achieved and Britain, pre-Boer War, was relatively stable. While unification across Europe was the order of the day, Ireland bucked the trend and gained a commitment from William Gladstone to introduce Home Rule, a promise that would ultimately bring thousands of Irish volunteers into World War I.

The build-up to the war in terms of the rivalry between the British and German fleets commenced in earnest following the development of the British Dreadnought battleship in 1906, soon to be imitated by the Germans.

Above: The *Twin Brothers* ran ashore at Ballinacourty Lighthouse, Dungarvan, Co. Waterford, in April 1909. Built in 1865, the 109-ton, two-masted schooner operated as a coastal trader, carrying coal and other goods around Britain and Ireland for almost 44 years before it was wrecked. The crew managed to row ashore in the ship's boat. (Ian Lawler Collection)

This sparked an arms race, with bigger and stronger battleships being built and major fleet expansion on both sides. This rivalry between the fleets continued until the outbreak of war in 1914, following the assassination of Archduke Franz Ferdinand in Sarajevo and the almost immediate mobilisation of the rival alliances, with Britain, France and Russia on one side versus Germany and the Austro-Hungarian empire on the other. The build-up to the conflict at sea also saw the development of the submarine as an essential instrument of war. The submarine developed very quickly following the successful launch of Irish-American John Philip Holland's prototype in New York harbour just a few years earlier, in 1898. By the start of World War I the submarine was seen as a key part of the naval strategy to control the high seas, particularly by the Germans. Of course, that is another story and it is told in Chapter 4. In this chapter, the many documented losses of the modern historic period are recounted, charting a devastating period in Ireland's maritime history.

Rutland Island Wreck

Compiled by Connie Kelleher

GSI ref. code	299
NMS wreck no.	W11641
Location	100m off SE shore of Rutland Island, Burtonport, Co. Donegal
Co-ordinates	54 58 18N; 008 26 38W
Depth of water	5m
Vessel type	Possible Spanish Armada ship
Vessel dimensions	18m (l), 6m (b), 1.4m (d)
Date of building	*c.* 16th century
Date of loss	possibly 1588

Circumstances of loss

The Rutland Island Wreck, as it is currently known, is located in shallow waters off the SE shore of Rutland Island and has been the focus of survey and investigation by the UAU since the summer of 2010. Local divers from Burtonport discovered the wreck in late 2009. The remains are located approximately 100m offshore and to the NW of the old navigation channel that led into the pier at Burtonport. The wreck site lies at a depth that ranges between 3m at the stern end and 5m at the bow, and is orientated E–W, with the bow to the W, facing the Rutland shoreline. How the ship met its fate in this area remains unknown, but it would have stood well proud of the water when it wrecked and thus subject to intensive salvage throughout the intervening centuries. What remains today is the lower hull section, with the ship having come to rest on its starboard side. A large part of the lower starboard hull survives, up to the beginning of the orlop deck. The vessel collapsed to starboard, spilling its contents to the N; the lower levels of the port side are elevated, with a large section of the lower transom, sternpost and rudder remaining. To the immediate SE of the bow area, a deep scour pit is visible leading out into deeper water, where further scattered remains of the wreck have been found and artefactual material recovered.

On the seafloor

In the summer of 2011 the Minister for Arts, Heritage and the Gaeltacht, Mr Jimmy Deenihan TD, granted specific

Above: Broken bow of the Rutland Island Wreck can be seen partially exposed on the seabed, with a scatter of oven bricks that would have come from the upper galley area in the ship, which has since been lost. (Photo Connie Kelleher)

funding to carry out a more intensive excavation of the wreck site in order to recover artefacts that remained within the wreck itself. A collaborative project ensued, with the GSI/INFOMAR working with the UAU on site and supplying the RV *Keary* and her crew for the duration of the project. The seabed mapping of the wreck site was carried out by the RV *Geo* and the National Museum of Ireland is conserving the artefactual material that is being recovered from the wreck site.

Archaeological excavation at the site focused on opening up the stern area of the wreck, with two other test trenches opened at mid-ships and at the bow. From artefacts recovered, it appears that this is the remains of a 16th-century vessel; preliminary analysis of some of the recovered

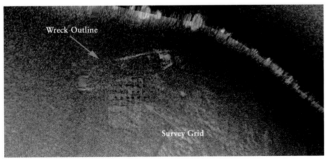

Above: Diver recording the stern end of the wreck after it has been excavated. (Photo Connie Kelleher)

Left: Side-scan sonar image showing the outline of the wreck, which stands proud of the seabed. The UAU survey and excavation grid can be seen to the N of wreck site, prior to it being moved fully over the wreck.

pottery suggests an Iberian origin. What can be said with certainty is that the Rutland Island Wreck was an armed vessel that was involved in conflict at sea, as evidenced by the musket shot and cannon balls recovered from the lower hold and from the debris field to the SE, which includes flattened lead shot that may have been fired at some stage.

A number of possible explanations as to the ship's identity present themselves, including a strong possibility that the wreck is linked to the ill-fated Spanish Armada campaign of 1588; several of the Armada ships were recorded as being wrecked along the general coastline in this area. In tandem with the present archaeological evidence, a 1799 *Naval Chronicle* account tells of the salvage, in 1793, of a Spanish Armada wreck that was located in the shallows of Rutland harbour, with the bronze guns recovered at the time bearing the crest of

Philip II of Spain. Alternatively, the wreck could be a previously unknown armed merchant ship or pirate vessel, many of which would have frequented the north-western coastal havens of Donegal in that period. It may perhaps have been associated with the Gaelic Lordships of Uí Bhaoill or Uí Mháille, and therefore would have plied the waters between Ireland and the Continent, trading, raiding and engaging with other ships and fleets during its voyages at sea. The UAU, in collaboration with the GSI/INFOMAR and the NMI, intends to return to the Rutland Island wreck site in 2012 to carry out further investigation and survey work, with analysis, dendrochronological dating and research ongoing on artefacts and samples recovered to date from the wreck site.

Printed Sources

Anon. 1799, 291
Donnelly 1999
Kelleher 2010
Kelleher 2011, 38-40

La Surveillante

GSI ref. code	258
NMS wreck no.	W08507
Location	Bantry Bay, 1.2 miles NW of Whiddy Island, Co. Cork
Co-ordinates	51 42 13.77N, 009 32 28.03W
Depth of water	30m
Vessel type	Frigate
Vessel dimensions	43.55m (l), 11.21m (b), 5.68m (d)
Date of building	1778
Date of loss	2 January 1797

Circumstances of loss

La Surveillante was a 620-ton French frigate built in Lorient in 1778. It measured 43m in length and carried 32 guns. The vessel had three masts and was copper sheathed to protect the hull from damage by marine organisms. The vessel was involved in a number of successful naval engagements with British warships during the American War of Independence (1775–82). However, *La Surveillante*

is probably best known for its defeat of the English frigate *Quebec* in 1779, off the coast of Ushant. In 1796 *La Surveillante* took part in the unsuccessful attempt by France to invade Ireland. The enterprise seemed doomed from the outset, with bad weather and poor leadership resulting in the 48-strong French invasion fleet being scattered and dispersed. Although most of the storm-battered fleet arrived off Bantry, Co. Cork, on 19 December, continued bad weather, poor decision-making by the captains and further loss of ships forced the fleet to return to France without ever setting foot on Irish soil. *La Surveillante* was considered unseaworthy for the return journey and was scuttled by its crew in Bantry Bay. Its crew and all 600 cavalry and troops on board were transferred safely to other French ships in the fleet. Of the 48 ships that left Brest on 16 December 1796, only 36 returned to France: the rest were either captured by the English Navy or wrecked.

Below: Survey plan of the wreck site, as recorded during a survey and excavation by the Centre for Maritime Archaeology, University of Ulster, and the Underwater Archaeology Unit in 1999. (Courtesy of Colin Breen)

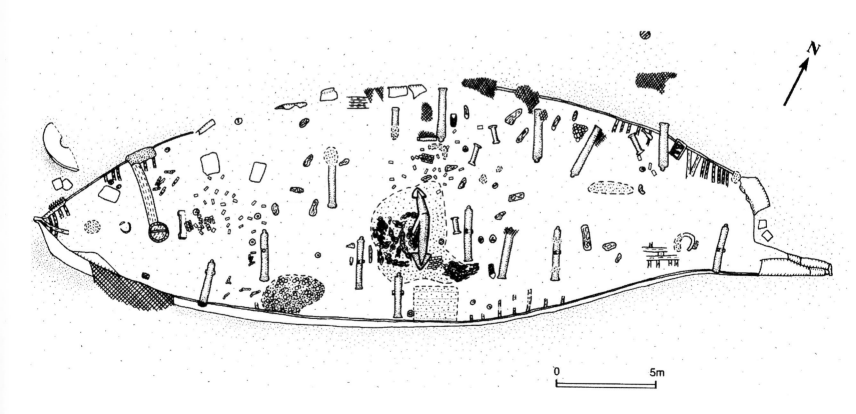

On the seafloor

The wreck of *La Surveillante* was discovered in 1981 during seabed clearance operations following the *Betelgeuse* oil tanker disaster. Two years earlier, in 1979, the *Betelgeuse* had caught fire and blew up at the Whiddy oil terminal, with the loss of 60 lives. Prior to this, one of *La Surveillante*'s anchors had been trawled up by fishermen and put on display in Bantry, but the presence of the wreck itself had remained unknown, until the events in 1979–81. In 1987 two 12-pound cannons were raised from the wreck, and in 1997 the UAU lifted the ship's bell. The bell is currently on display in the Bantry Armada Centre, at Bantry House. The wreck of *La Surveillante* measures 42m in length, 10m in width and 4.3m in maximum height and is orientated NE–SW, with her bow to the NE. Copper sheathing is visible along the length of the wreck. The galley area, cannon, cannon balls and an anchor are also visible on the wreck.

Printed Sources

Breen, C. 2001

Quinn *et al.* 2002

Above: Robert Dodd's painting (1781) of *La Surveillante* and HMS *Quebec* off Ushant, on October 1779. After a furious battle both ships ended up de-masted, with heavy loss of life. The *Quebec* (*at right*) caught fire after accidentally firing through her own sails. Her surviving sailors were rescued by the victorious *La Surveillante* (*left*). (Courtesy of the National Maritime Museum, Greenwich)

Below: 3D multibeam image of *La Surveillante*, which lies partially buried in silt in 34m of water in Bantry Bay.

Queen Victoria

GSI ref. code	144a
NMS wreck no.	W00910
Location	1km SE of Howth Head, off the coast of Co. Dublin
Co-ordinates	53 21 36.22N, 006 3 3.71W
Depth of water	16m
Vessel dimensions	46m (l), 7m (b)
Date of building	1837
Date of loss	15 February 1853

Circumstances of loss

One of the more significant ships lost in Dublin Bay, the *Queen Victoria* was a 337-ton, 150-foot-long paddle steamer built in Liverpool in 1837. It was owned by the City of Dublin Steam Packet Company and was capable of 11 knots with 250 horse-power, diagonal compound engines. Under the command of Captain Church, the *Queen Victoria* departed Liverpool in fine weather on Monday, 14 February 1853, en route to Dublin with a general cargo, a voyage it had made numerous times without incident. On board the vessel were 24 crewmen, 12 cabin passengers, 75 deck passengers and one stewardess, totalling 112 persons. On approach to Dublin Bay the vessel encountered a snowstorm, which obscured the lights of both the Baily and Kish lighthouses. In spite of the poor visibility, the steamer failed to reduce its speed. It ran aground on the cliffs below the Baily Lighthouse, on Howth Head. At that point, about eight people were able to scramble ashore safely. The steamer then reversed away from the cliffs in an attempt to run the vessel ashore. This manoeuvre proved fatal, and the *Queen Victoria* began to sink rapidly.

Confusion and panic ensued, as most of those aboard had been asleep below deck. Although there were four lifeboats on board, only the port lifeboat managed to launch successfully in the challenging conditions the crew were facing. The *Queen Victoria* sank slowly into the dark, cold waters, drowning most of those who remained aboard. The single lifeboat made it safely to shore with 17 rescued people, then returned to try to find any remaining survivors. By that stage, only the mastheads and funnel were visible above water, with survivors clinging desperately to the masts. The lifeboat managed to rescue five of these tenacious individuals, while the steamer *Roscommon* rescued the others. A further eight brave passengers were able to make it ashore by swimming.

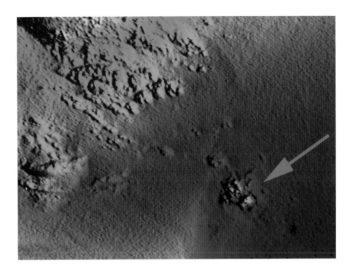

Above: High-resolution, multibeam view of the *Queen Victoria* and surrounding seabed. The poorly preserved remains (*highlighted by red arrow*) do not show up well in the multibeam data. The rocky seabed (*top*) is the base of the Baily promontory, upon which the paddle steamer ran aground before reversing off and sinking 230m S of the Baily Lighthouse.

The *Roscommon* saved about 40 passengers in total. There are differing accounts as to how many on board were lost, suggesting that between 50 and 83 may have drowned, including Captain Church.

On the seafloor

The wreck was rediscovered by Marlin Sub Aqua Club in 1983 and has been surveyed by a number of Dublin dive clubs since then. It now lies in around 18m of water in an area of strong tides, 230m S of the Baily Lighthouse, and is orientated NW–SE on the seafloor. It measures 17.5m in length, 7.5m in width, with a maximum height of 3.4m. The remains of the vessel are largely broken up, with debris and remains of the paddle wheels and boiler clearly visible on the seabed. A number of artefacts have been recovered from the wreck site, and the ship's figurehead is presently housed in the Maritime Museum in Dún Laoghaire, Co. Dublin. The *Queen Victoria* is one of less than a handful of paddle steamers that are diveable around the Irish coast.

Printed Sources

Bourke 1994, 20
Brady 2008, 202; 211–13
De Courcy Ireland 1983, 55–7

Hocking 1969, 573
Larn 1981, 140–42
UKHO Wreck Data 1996

Opposite: A coloured engraving by Chavanne graphically illustrating the sinking of the mail steam packet *Queen Victoria*, with the loss of around 80 lives. (Courtesy of the National Maritime Museum, Greenwich)

Sir Charles Napier

GSI ref. code	280
NMS wreck no.	W01588
Location	Kish Bank, off the coast of Co. Dublin
Co-ordinates	53 15 43.5N, 05 55 30.39W
Depth of water	7.9m
Vessel type	Full-rigged ship
Date of building	1841
Date of loss	19 November 1857

Circumstances of loss

The *Sir Charles Napier* was a 638-ton merchant vessel built in Miramichi, New Brunswick, Canada, and owned by Locketts of London. The sailing ship was en route from Liverpool to Sierra Leone, carrying a cargo that included 6,000 iron pots and iron hoops, when it was stranded and wrecked on the Kish Bank during a force 6 wind. The Kish Bank is but one of a series of underwater sandbanks that run parallel to the east coast of Ireland, stretching from Wexford in the south to Dublin Bay in the north. One of the most treacherous of these sandbanks is the Kish Bank. Master Samuel Bissett and 18 of his crew survived; one crew member was drowned. The vessel was clearly off-course

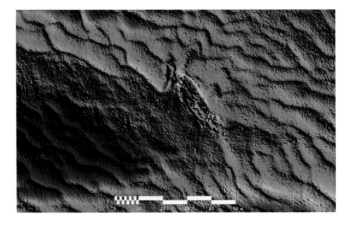

Above: Multibeam image of the *Sir Charles Napier* lying NW–SE on a sandy seabed on the Kish Bank, in a general sea depth of 8m.

when lost and a subsequent inquiry in Dublin found that the ship's compass had been affected by the large cargo of iron carried on board, a problem compounded by carelessness on the master's part in navigating the vessel. It was estimated that the value of the loss of the vessel was £3,000, with another £4,000 lost on the cargo.

On the seafloor

The *Sir Charles Napier* measures 33m in length, 7m in width and 1.7m in maximum height and lies orientated NW–SE on a sandy seabed in a general sea depth of 8m. A survey by Roy Stokes of Marlin Sub Aqua Club in 2003 identified the wreck as that of the *Sir Charles Napier*. Even though the wreck was partially salvaged at the time, part of the cargo still remains on board, including crockery, iron skillets and faggots of iron.

Printed Sources
Brady 2008, 306, 310
Lloyd's Register 1857, S 439
PP 1857–1858, LII, 9
PP 1859, XXV, 37
PP 1861, LVII, 36
Stokes 2003/4, 18–20

Internet Source
www.irishwrecks.com

Above: A winch located on the bow of the wreck. (Photo Graham Stokes)

Glenorchy (Possibly)

GSI ref. code	277
NMS wreck no.	W01572
Location	Kish Bank, off the coast of Co. Dublin
Co-ordinates	53 16 50.10N, 005 55 59.4W
Depth of water	6.75m
Vessel type	Iron Sailing ship
Vessel dimensions	60m (l), 20m (b), 5m (d)
Date of building	November 1868
Date of loss	1 January 1869

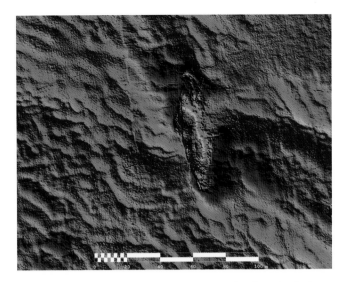

Above: Multibeam image of the 70m long wreck of the *Glenorchy*. The force of the currents and tidal movements that helped form the Kish Bank are illustrated by sand waves and scour holes around the site. Although largely buried to its gunnels, its cargo of machinery remains *in situ* and stands over 3m high (*red areas inside wreck*).

Circumstances of loss

The *Glenorchy* was a Glasgow-registered, 1,285-ton iron merchant sailing ship. It was built by A. McMillan & Sons Ltd. in Dumbarton for Allan & Gow (McGregor & Gow) of Glasgow. Like many ships of its time, the *Glenorchy* was lost on its maiden voyage due to a combination of bad weather, human error and the crew's lack of familiarity with the ship's equipment.

The *Glenorchy* left Greenock under the command of Thomas Meiklejohn on 17 December, headed for Bombay with a cargo of coal, railway sleepers and £100,000 worth of railway machinery. It made slow progress, with bad weather forcing it to put into Rothesay and Lamlash, on the Isle of Arran. It eventually resumed its journey but shortly after passing Holyhead Bay, the wind increased to gale force, with drizzle reducing visibility. The *Glenorchy* continued on its south-westerly heading until it ran aground on the Kish Bank. The stricken vessel displayed its blue lights and fired rockets, but poor visibility prevented them from being seen on shore until ten o'clock that night, when residents of Kingstown (now Dún Laoghaire) heard the distress signals. In the ensuing panic, one of the lifeboats was washed away while being launched, while a crew member was injured when attempting to lower another boat. The crew of the *Glenorchy* were eventually saved, with the captain and 14 men being towed to Dún Laoghaire in a lifeboat by a Dublin pilot tug, while the rest of the crew reached the Kish Lightship in another boat. A number of attempts were made by tugs to salvage cargo from the vessel and some trawlers managed to remove rigging and sails off the vessel. The master of the *Glenorchy* blamed erroneous compass readings for their misfortune, claiming this diverted the vessel off-course, but a subsequent inquiry laid the blame with the ship's master for failing to take account of the weather and tidal conditions.

On the seafloor

The wreck of the *Glenorchy* is buried to its gunnels on the starboard side, with much of the port side visible, along with some plating lying on the seabed. Machinery and the iron mast remain *in situ*. Some of the iron cargo and liquor bottles are also evident. The wreck measures 70m in length, 13m in width and 3.3m in maximum height and lies orientated N–S on a sandy seabed in a general sea depth of 7m, with its bow lying to the N.

Printed Sources
Anon. 2005, 5
Brady 2008, 304
The Irish Times and *Daily Advertiser*, 4 January 1869
Lloyd's Register 1869, G 312
PP 1870 LX, 98
PP 1871 LXI, 38

Internet Source
www.irishwrecks.com

HMS Vanguard

GSI ref. code	247
NMS wreck no.	W02099
Location	15m SE of Dún Laoghaire, Co. Dublin
Co-ordinates	53 12 46.666N, 005 46 18.742W
Depth of water	45m
Vessel type	Ironclad battleship
Vessel dimensions	85.34m (l), 16.46m (b), 7.31m (d)
Date of building	September 1870
Date of loss	1 September 1875

Circumstances of loss

The HMS *Vanguard* was one of four Audacious class, ironclad battleships built by Cammel Laird & Co. at Birkenhead, England, at a cost of £355,000. The 6,034-ton vessel was powered by steam and sail and was capable of attaining speeds up to 14 knots. The 6-inch-thick iron hull was reinforced along its waterline and an iron ram was attached to the bow below the waterline. Her armoury included both 6-inch and 9-inch guns. It was completed in September 1870 and commissioned into service as a guardship at Kingstown (now Dún Laoghaire).

On 1 September 1875 the *Vanguard*, under the command of Captain Richard Dawkins, went to sea on manoeuvres with five other ironclad battleships of the Reserve Squadron of the Channel Fleet and the yacht *Hawk*. Shortly after departing Kingstown for Queenstown (now Cobh), Co. Cork, the formation encountered thick fog and the *Vanguard* was accidentally rammed by her sister ship, HMS *Iron Duke*. As water flowed into the damaged battleship, her internal compartments were incapable of containing the flow and she began to sink. The boiler furnaces were soon extinguished, depriving her of power, and within an hour the *Vanguard* sank. Fortunately, no lives were lost in this incident as the 360 men on board managed to get safely into lifeboats and board the *Iron Duke*. The *Iron Duke*, with its bow damaged, returned to Dún Laoghaire. Nine days later a court martial was quickly convened on board the HMS *Adelaide*, during which Captain Dawkins and four of his officers were severely reprimanded for failing to save the ship. Limited salvage work was carried out on the wreck

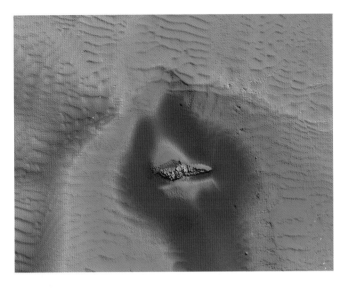

Above left: High-resolution, multibeam view of the wreck of the HMS *Vanguard* and surrounding seabed. A 400m long scour has developed to the S of the 93m long wreck, indicating the strong currents and tidal movements that are continuously wearing away the iron-clad warship.

Above right: High-resolution, 3D, multibeam view of the wreck from the S shows that it is intact and standing 15m proud of the surrounding seabed. It lists slightly towards her starboard side and is oriented E–W on a sandy seabed in general sea depth of 45m.

and attempts by the British Admiralty to raise it came to nothing due to difficult and dangerous diving conditions.

On the seafloor

The wreck of the HMS *Vanguard* measures 93m in length, 14m in width and 15m in maximum height. The vessel lies E–W on a sandy seabed in a general sea depth of 45m and lists slightly towards her starboard side. In conditions of good visibility – most commonly experienced early in the diving season, in May – the *Vanguard* is one of the most spectacular shipwrecks in Ireland. The wreck is very intact, but has broken its back aft of the box battery, where there is a 2m split, and sits with a list of 30 degrees to starboard. The damage caused by the *Iron Duke*'s ram is clearly visible on the port side forward of the box battery, and coal is strewn around the seabed in this area. The stump of the mainmast leads out into the scour pit to starboard. When she was first dived in the 1980s, it was possible to enter the main deck through the break and swim all the way aft and exit through the officers' quarters, but now the top deck has collapsed down and slid to starboard, which has also caused the 2m port gunwales to collapse. On the collapsed aft top deck the remains of the helm position, which once held very intact 2m teak and brass wheels and the capstan, are also prominent. The port Griffiths screw – a very early and strange-looking propeller design – is well worth a visit. Its starboard partner is now nearly buried under sand and collapsing wreckage

Above: Engraving published in the *Graphic* on 11 September 1875 of the HMS *Vanguard* (sinking on the right) shortly after the accidental collision. The crew of the *Vanguard* can be seen in the lifeboats, making their way to the HMS *Iron Duke* in the foreground, the vessel that rammed their stricken ship. (Ian Lawler Collection)

down in the scour, at 50m. In the box battery itself some of the main deck 9-inch muzzle-loaders are visible if you venture into the break, but a number have now collapsed down into the bowels of the wreck. The most easily seen are the two oblique firing guns on the port top deck of the battery, at around 35m. Forward the 2m gunwales are still intact and a 64lb chaser gun and an anchor are to be found on the port bow. The bow itself is majestic in good visibility, with the underwater ram clearly visible, below the point of which sits another enormous anchor.

Printed Sources
Brady 2008, 370, 385–6, 405–7
Larn & Larn 2002
Thomas 2006

Vesper

GSI ref. code	284
NMS wreck no.	W01594
Location	Kish Bank, off the coast of Co. Dublin
Co-ordinates	53 16 5.66N, 5 55 46.24W
Depth of water	8.65m
Vessel type	Iron Steamship
Vessel dimensions	58m (l), 5.5m (b)
Date of building	1866
Date of loss	13 January 1876

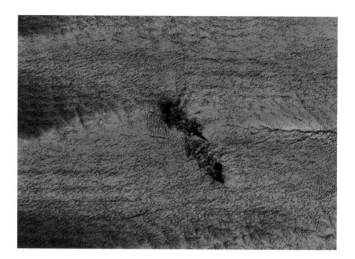

Above: Multibeam image of the 54m long wreck lying in a general sea depth of 8m. Large sand waves are threatening to completely bury the wreck in sand. It is already largely buried at its stern and amidships, whereas a small scour has exposed the bow and focs'le area.

Circumstances of loss

The *Vesper* was a 478-ton (gross tonnage) iron merchant steamer of Hartlepool, built in Dundee by Barclay Curle & Company, with a nominal horse-power of 60. Benjamin R. Huntley of Hartlepool was one of the vessel's owners. The ship's master was Jacob Tolsen and under his command the *Vesper* left Glasgow on 11 January 1876, en route to Dunkirk in France, carrying 600 tonnes of coal and sugar. All was going well until the early hours of the morning of 13 January, when the vessel struck the Kish Bank and became stranded. Signals of distress fired by the stricken vessel were not responded to and after a number of unsuccessful attempts to get the steamer off the sandbank, the vessel began to break in two. After three failed attempts to launch the lifeboats, the ship's captain and crew of 16 eventually managed to launch a lifeboat and landed safely at Killiney, Co. Dublin. The captain blamed the sinking on a defective compass. A subsequent inquiry held that Master Tolsen had failed to take the necessary precautions when approaching waters well known to be dangerous. Both Tolsen and his chief officer were severely reprimanded for altering the logbook in an effort to mislead the inquiry as to the ship's correct position in relation to land. Master Tolsen was required to pay £5 towards the cost of the inquiry.

On the seafloor

The wreck of the *Vesper* lies in a general sea depth of 8m and measures 54m in length, 9m in width and 2.27m in maximum height. The vessel lies on a sandy seabed, orientated N–S, with its stern to the N. The southern end of the wreck is mostly buried, but the outlines of the stern and of the boiler area are visible. The bow and focs'le area are the most prominent parts of the wreck and stand largely intact and proud of the seabed, with anchors and winches visible.

Above: Diver exploring the bow of the *Vesper*. (Photo Graham Stokes)

Printed Sources
Brady 2008, 306
Browne & Stokes 2009, 11–12
The Irish Times, 14 January 1876
PP 1876, LXVII, 45, 219, 395–6

Internet Source
www.irishwrecks.com

Flying Dart

GSI ref. code	135
NMS wreck no.	W00883/W01549
Location	3km SE of the Baily Lighthouse, Dublin Bay
Co-ordinates	053 20 50.74N, 06 00 39.1W
Depth of water	28m
Vessel type	Iron Paddle Steam Tug
Vessel dimensions	30.5m (l), 5.51m (b), 2.86m (d)
Date of building	1882
Date of loss	12 August 1890

Above: Photograph of the *Flying Dart*, by G.E. Langmuir, passing Mirren Quay, Port Glasgow.

Circumstances of loss

The *Flying Dart* was a 111-ton iron paddle steam tug, built by J.T. Eltringham, South Shields, with 70 horse-power engines. It was owned by the Clyde Company (G. Kidston of Glasgow) and the ship's master was J. Altrum. The vessel was en route, in ballast, from Dún Laoghaire to Dublin Bay in adverse weather conditions when it collided with a cattle steamship, the *North Wall* of Dublin, belonging to the London and North-Western Railway Company. The *Flying Dart* sank about 20 minutes after the accident, though the *North Wall* apparently sustained no damage. The six crew on board the tug were rescued by lifeboats despatched by the *North Wall*.

On the seafloor

The wreck of the *Flying Dart* measures 27.7m in length, 4m in width and is orientated E–W in a general depth of 28m. It is almost completely buried in the muddy, sandy seabed, the gunwale aft protruding only a few centimeters. However, amidships the boiler is clearly visible, with its central hole for the funnel, as are the remains of the paddle wheels to either side. As you move forward the hull is more exposed, leading to a small scour around the bow, which stands 1m high. The wreck lies directly under the route taken by the fast ferry, *Jonathan Swift*, on its way into and out of Dublin Port. It is therefore essential to check the ferry timetable as well as the tide tables before diving it.

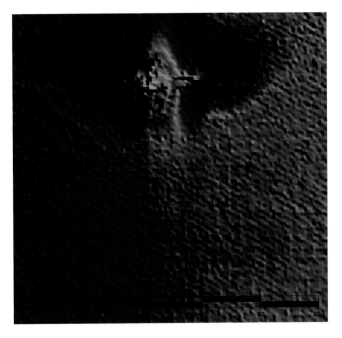

Above: Multibeam image of the wreck of the *Flying Dart*, located 3km SE of the Baily Lighthouse. The vessel lies upright on the seabed, with areas of deep scouring around both ends of the vessel.

Printed Sources

Brady 2008, 200
The Irish Times, 13 August 1890
The Irish Times, 14 August 1890
Lloyd's Register 1883–84, F 305
PP 1892, LXXI, 142

SS Premier

Above: A badly faded and damaged postcard of the *Premier* in dock. It has not been possible to confirm whether this *Premier* is the Limerick Steamship Company steamer that was wrecked in the Shannon Estuary in November 1898. (Ian Lawler Collection)

GSI ref. code	253
NMS wreck no.	W06353
Location	River Shannon, 2km NW of Beal Point, Co. Kerry
Co-ordinates	52 35 31.8N, 009 38 31.2W
Depth of water	21.6m
Vessel type	Cargo Vessel
Vessel dimensions	53.4m (l), 8.32m (b), 4m (d)
Date of building	1894
Date of loss	26 November 1898

Circumstances of loss

The SS *Premier* was a 537-ton cargo steamship, built in 1894 by J. Shearer & Sons, Kelvinhaugh, Glasgow. It measured 53m in length and had a two-cylinder steam compound engine with one boiler. At the time of its loss it was owned by J. Simpson of Glasgow and was under charter to the Limerick Steamship Company, with a 600-ton cargo of sugar for Messrs Cleeve of Limerick. The vessel was captained by D. Murray and had a crew numbering 14. On the final leg of its journey, from Hamburg to Limerick, it was involved in a collision in the Shannon Estuary with the paddle steamer *Mermaid*, of Waterford, between Scattery Island and Kilcredaun Point. It is unclear how the collision happened, but the *Mermaid*, which was outbound from Limerick to Waterford, struck the *Premier* on the port side, tearing open her plates. The *Premier* sank within 15 minutes and its crew, who had taken to the lifeboats, were picked up by a passing steamer, the *Vanda*. The *Mermaid*'s bow was badly damaged and it was forced to return to Limerick for repairs. The wreck of the *Premier* is now known locally as 'The Sugar Boat'.

On the seafloor

The wreck of the SS *Premier* measures 53m in length, 8m in width and 5.4m in maximum height. The vessel is orientated NE–SW on the seabed in a general depth of 21m. The site is subject to strong tidal currents and is located in the main shipping channel.

Printed Sources

The Irish Times, 28 November 1898
Larn & Larn 2002
Lloyd's List 19, 103, 28 November 1898; 19, 123, 21 December 1898; 19, 125, 23 December 1898
PP 1900 LXXVII, 154
UKHO Wreck Data 1996

Below: High-resolution, multibeam view of the SS *Premier*. It measures 53m long and lies almost mid-channel in the Shannon Estuary, in a general depth of 21m. The vessel lies NE–SW on the seabed, with its bow to the SW and the highest part of the wreck, at the stern, to the NE (*red and grey patches*).

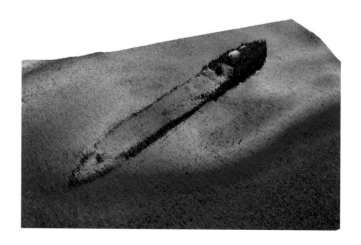

Marlay

GSI ref. code	249
NMS wreck no.	W02049
Location	approx. 4km NE of the Nose of Howth, Co. Dublin
Co-ordinates	53 23 18.05N, 005 58 38.16W
Depth of water	27m
Vessel type	Cargo Vessel
Vessel dimensions	61m (l), 8.8m (b), 4.3m (d)
Date of building	1890
Date of loss	16 December 1902

Circumstances of loss

The *Marlay* was a 798-ton, 61m long steel steam collier, built in 1890 by Workman Clarke & Co. of Belfast. It was owned by Dublin coal merchants Tedcastle, McCormick & Co. and had a compound expansion engine delivering 170 nominal horse-power. The *Marlay*, under the command of Captain J. Hamilton of Liverpool, left Liverpool for Dublin at 2.00pm on Monday, 15 December 1902 with a 900-ton cargo of coal. After passing Holyhead, the *Marlay*'s progress was slowed by stormy weather and heavy seas. The ferocity of the storm increased as the *Marlay* neared the Irish coast and the crew were forced to man the pumps as the vessel began to take on water through leaking hatches. By 4.00am conditions had got so bad, Captain Hamilton gave the order to man the lifeboats as the vessel was listing to the starboard side. Able seaman Michael McGlue tried to lower the starboard lifeboat, but a huge wave smashed into the port side of the vessel, washing the starboard lifeboat overboard, with McGlue clinging grimly on to it. McGlue struggled to climb into the lifeboat, but was unable to get back to the *Marlay* because of the intensity of the storm. The *Marlay* sank within five minutes, with the loss of all 15 men remaining on board. McGlue was the sole survivor. He was picked up, still in the lifeboat, by passing steam trawler *Peter Johnson* near Rockabill at 10.15am and brought to Dublin. This tragic episode led to the foundation of a Widow and Orphans Fund to help the 11 wives who were left widowed and the 49 children who were left fatherless as a result of the loss of the *Marlay*.

On the seafloor

The wreck of the *Marlay*, orientated NE–SW, measures 61m in length, 10.5m in width and 7.14m in maximum height. The vessel lies in a general sea depth of 27m, largely buried on the starboard side, with its bow pointing towards the SW. The hull of the *Marlay* is largely intact, though the superstructure has collapsed. Its cargo of coal lies scattered around the wreck.

Printed Sources

Brady 2008, 380

de Courcy Ireland 1983, 131

Freeman's Journal, 17 December 1902, 5

Hocking 1969, 456

The Irish Times, 17 December 1902; 18 December 1902; 19 December 1902; 22 December 1902; 27 December 1902; 24 January 1903; 6 February 1903; 7 February 1903; 14 February 1903; 28 February 1903; 11 June 1903

Lloyd's List 20,362, 17 December 1902; 20,373, 31 December 1902; 20,374, 1 January 1903; 20,480, 6 May 1903

PP 1904, LXXXVI, 110

Below: The largely intact hull of the *Marlay* shows up well against the soft, muddy and sandy seabed of the Irish Sea. The 3D multibeam imagery shows large areas of scouring *(coloured purple)* that have developed around the wreck, indicating the strong currents and tidal movements in the area.

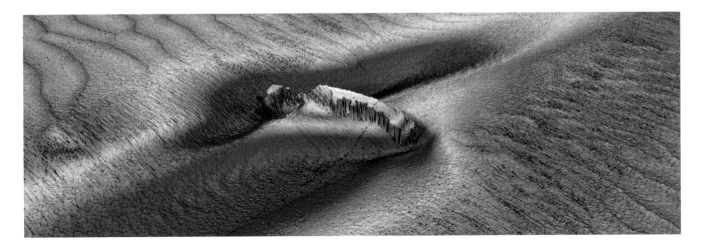

SS Manchester Merchant

GSI ref. code	248
NMS wreck no.	W05784
Location	4.5km WNW of Rosbehy Point, Dingle Bay, Co. Kerry
Co-ordinates	52 05 43.2N, 010 1 58.8W
Depth of water	11.3m
Vessel type	Cargo Ship/War Transport
Vessel dimensions	137.77m (l), 15.9m (b), 8.62m (d)
Date of building	1900
Date of loss	15 January 1903

Circumstances of loss

The SS *Manchester Merchant* was built in 1900 by Palmer's Shipbuilding and Iron Company Ltd., Newcastle-upon-Tyne. The 5,657-ton vessel was propelled by a 642 horse-power, triple expansion engine, as well as four masts. Although originally built for the newly formed Manchester Liner Company Ltd., it was requisitioned by the British Government immediately after its completion to transport troops, supplies, horses and ammunition to South Africa during the Boer War (1899–1902). After the war the SS *Manchester Merchant* was returned to its

Above: A 3D, multibeam image of the SS *Manchester Merchant* lying on the seabed 4.5km WNW of Rosbehy Point, Dingle Bay, Co. Kerry. The internal structure of the wreck is visible, with high points at the bow and amidships where the remains of the boilers stand over 5m above the seabed.

Above: The SS *Manchester Merchant* under steam *c.*1900. (Courtesy of the National Maritime Museum, Greenwich)

owners. It was lost during its first voyage, while en route from New Orleans to Manchester with a cargo of 13,000 bales of cotton for the Lancashire cotton mills. The vessel, commanded by W.P. Couch and manned by a crew of 56, was also carrying 100 barrels of turpentine, soap, pitch, pine and grain.

It is believed that on 12 January 1903 the cotton cargo spontaneously ignited, with the vessel subsequently catching fire as it neared the southwest coast of Ireland. The cargo ship sought refuge in Dingle Bay and dropped anchor near the entrance to Castlemaine harbour. As the fire intensified, the fore part of the vessel was completely ablaze, forcing the crew to throw the turpentine overboard. With efforts to fight the fire proving fruitless, most of the crew took to the lifeboats, leaving the master and a handful of crew to scuttle the ship in shallow water, which they did on 15 January. There was no loss of life in this incident, but some of the crew suffered from smoke inhalation.

Despite subsequent attempts to refloat the vessel, the wreck had been declared a total loss by the end of February. Hundreds of cotton bales were salvaged, with many more washing ashore along the Kerry coastline in the following months; cotton and turpentine washed ashore even as far north as counties Mayo, Sligo and Donegal. The captain gave the ship's bell to locals as a token of gratitude for their assistance. The bell of the *Manchester Merchant* is housed in the Roman Catholic church at Anascaul, Co. Kerry.

On the seafloor

The wreck of the SS *Manchester Merchant* lies in over 11m of water and is orientated NE–SW, with its bow to the NE. It lies largely intact and measures 157m in length and 18m in width. There is hull plating scattered on the seabed on either side of the wreck. The boilers still stand abaft of amidships and are the highest part of the wreck, with a maximum height of 5.3m above the seabed.

Printed Sources

Hocking 1969, 448
IFC S 426, 509; 437, 35, 199; 476, 59
Larn & Larn 2002
Lloyd's List 15 January 1903–18 September 1903
PP 1904, Vol. LXXXVI, 149

Following pages: The crew of a U-boat look on as the vessel they just torpedoed sinks stern first beneath the waves. (Ian Lawler Collection)

4 Ireland and World War I

James Lyttleton, Roy Stokes and Karl Brady

War and Conflict off the Irish Coast, 1914–1918

The role played by Ireland during World War I has been largely ignored in mainstream history books, until recently. This is understandable given the political context of the time and the ensuing struggle for independence from British rule, which overshadowed everything else thereafter. However, in recent years there has been a gradual realisation and acceptance of the significance and importance of the part played by Irish men and women during one of the greatest conflicts in the history of the world. When war broke out in 1914, Ireland was part of the British Empire, and over 200,000 Irishmen enlisted and fought for British, American and Canadian armies. Sadly, 30,000 Irish men and women lost their lives on the battlefields of Europe. Nonetheless, Irish divisions and regiments made a major contribution to the war effort and to a number of the major battles, campaigns and offences, including Gallipoli, Ypres, Messines and the battle of the Somme.

In much the same manner that the Irish war effort has long been misinterpreted or misunderstood, to date there has been relatively little understanding or appreciation of the conflict that played out in the coastal waters around Ireland between 1914 and 1918. Thankfully, this oversight is now being addressed. A renewed interest in our maritime heritage, along with greater capabilities to explore our seas, has seen the story of this great seaborne conflict gradually come to light. The numerous shipwrecks that lie scattered to the north and south of Ireland are testimony to this violent period in Ireland's maritime history, highlighting for us a time of threat, danger, intrigue and loss.

Lying astride the western approaches to British ports, Ireland was of significant strategic interest to the warring European powers. In an attempt to hinder Britain's international trade, the Imperial German Navy – the *Kaiserliche Marine* – orchestrated a deadly submarine offensive, which led to the waters to the north and south of Ireland becoming known as 'killing lanes'. As a result, the protection enjoyed by Allied maritime traffic by virtue of travelling in the broad expanse of the Atlantic was lost as soon as it entered the narrowing approaches to the north and south of Ireland. Despite protests over the loss of neutral and unarmed ships, the attacks by the *Kaiserliche Marine* continued. The battle they waged took a dreadful toll: it is estimated that there are at least 1,800 shipwrecks in the waters surrounding Ireland dating to the years of this conflict.

In turn, Britain sought to obstruct Germany's access to global maritime trade by instigating a policy of blockade, with the Royal Navy largely restricting German naval and merchant fleets to the North Sea and the Baltic Sea. German submarines arrived in the waters separating Ireland and England to disrupt Ireland's supply of food and war materials for the British war effort. Ships plying their trade in Irish waters had to contend with the threat posed by U-boats and their deadly deck guns and torpedoes, and even when in sight of home they ran the risk of hitting one of the many mines that had been laid by the German Navy across the approaches to harbours. It was a period of heightened tension, with every crossing by water fraught with danger and difficulty.

Although there were no engagements in Irish waters during 1914, the opening of hostilities caught Britain somewhat on the back foot elsewhere and the British Navy lost 22 important warships in that year. In the North Sea three capital ships, the HMS *Cressy*, *Hogue* and *Aboukir*, were sunk in quick succession off the Hook of Holland, on 22 September, by *U-9* with the loss of almost 1,500 personnel. As a result, the Royal Navy's Grand Fleet was shifted to more suitable havens on the northern and western coasts of the British Isles, such as Scapa Flow, an enclosed deepwater haven in the Orkney Islands, and Lough Swilly, Co. Donegal, with its long, enclosed

Opposite: The sinking of the *Lusitania* was used to promote recruitment to the British armed forces in Ireland and Britain, and as propaganda to help push American opinion towards joining the war effort against Germany. (Courtesy of the National Library of Ireland)

IRISHMEN
AVENGE THE LUSITANIA

JOIN AN IRISH REGIMENT
TO-DAY.

ISSUED BY THE CENTRAL COUNCIL FOR THE ORGANISATION OF RECRUITING IN IRELAND.   John Shuley & Co., Dublin.   Wt P. 110—7,500   5 15

Above: The SS *Manchester Commerce* was the first vessel to be sunk in Irish waters during WWI, when it encountered a German minefield off the north Donegal coast on 26 October 1914. The remains of a wreck, believed to be the SS *Manchester Commerce,* lie mangled on the seabed, although the rudder and propeller can still be seen. (Photo Barry McGill)

harbour. However, the security thought to be provided by distance proved to be illusory. In October the German liner *Berlin*, now armed as a cruiser, laid mines off Lough Swilly, resulting in the first sinking in Irish waters: the SS *Manchester Commerce*, on 26 October 1914. Two days later, while on manoeuvres, the same minefield claimed the only British capital battleship to be sunk in the entire conflict: HMS *Audacious* (*see* p.55). There was an attempt to hide these embarrassing and dangerous losses by converting a number of merchant vessels into a fleet of 'dummy battleships' (copies of actual ones), in order to confuse the enemy as to the actual disposition of the Navy's capital ships. But to the consternation of British officials, photographs were published in the USA of the *Audacious* as she sank, taken by passengers aboard the liner *Olympic*, which had come to the aid of the stricken vessel.

Given the stalemate on the Western Front, Germany commenced an unrestricted submarine campaign from 18 February 1915, with the waters around Britain and Ireland declared a war zone. U-boats roamed openly in these waters, sinking ships and shelling important on-shore targets. Enemy vessels, whether naval or mercantile, were attacked and sunk without warning; even neutral vessels entered these waters at their own risk. The British Navy had been caught unprepared, with few measures at its disposal to combat the new U-boat menace. This was not surprising as many in high office had heaped derision on the notion of U-boats attacking merchant or British naval vessels in home waters, considering the submarine to be the arm of a 'weaker power'. They surely came to regret those words.

The most famous loss in this unrestricted U-boat campaign was the Cunard-owned *Lusitania* (*see* p. 61), at the time one of the largest liners plying the transatlantic route. En route from New York to Liverpool, the vessel received warnings of U-boat activity off the Irish coast but failed to engage in zig-zagging manoeuvres to hinder potential attack. On 7 May 1915 the *Lusitania* sailed into the sight of *Kapitänleutnant* Walther Schwieger, commander of *U-20*. He duly attacked, firing a single torpedo that struck the hull, just below the ship's bridge. The *Lusitania* foundered and sank, with the loss of

1,198 lives from a total of 1,959 crew and passengers. This massive loss of civilians travelling on an ocean liner provoked international outcry, particularly from the USA, which had lost 123 of her citizens in the attack. This incident, along with the sinking of the *Arabic* (40 lives lost), 80km south of the Old Head of Kinsale, and of the *Hesperian* (32 lives lost), 137km south-west of Fastnet Rock, forced the Germans to restrict their attacks on merchant or neutral shipping, for fear of provoking the USA into declaring war on Germany.

Another early casualty in the war was the armed merchant cruiser *Viknor* (*see* p.58), formerly the *Viking* of the Scandinavian Viking Cruising Company, which sank 35km north of Tory Island, Co. Donegal, on 13 January 1915. The *Viknor* was part of the 10th Cruiser Squadron, whose job it was to enforce the blockade of Germany. A number of vessels, including the *Viknor*, were sent to the region of the Faroe Islands in January to intercept suspicious vessels, but were in fact on the look-

out for one vessel in particular. This was the Norwegian liner SS *Bergensfjord*, which had sailed from New York to Bergen on 2 January with certain passengers aboard who were onward bound for Berlin. A German national with a false passport was arrested before boarding the liner in New York, but discovering that there were more persons of interest on the vessel, US Department of Justice officials boarded a Revenue cutter and pursued the liner into the harbour. She was stopped and searched, resulting in the arrest of a further four German passengers. Notwithstanding their efforts, the man they were most anxious to capture remained elusive. This was the 'super spy', Lieutenant Count Botho von Wedell, who was keenly sought by British Naval Intelligence. Travelling under the American alias of 'Mr Spero', von Wedell's luck held out and the steamer was allowed to continue on its journey. When word of von Wedell's escape reached London a number of vessels, including the *Viknor*, were dispatched with all haste to intercept the SS *Bergensfjord*. Despite attempts by the liner to evade detection, she was intercepted by patrols east of the Faroes on 11 January. She was boarded by crew from the *Viknor* and von Wedell was arrested, along with six others. The *Bergensfjord* was taken to Kirkwall, in the Orkneys, while the *Viknor* was ordered back to Liverpool. On her journey down the west

Below: The sinking of *U-58* by USS *Fanning* and USS *Nicholson* in November 1917 was celebrated as a major naval success, being the first ever sinking of an enemy U-boat in US naval history. The Americans issued posters and postcards to commemorate the event, although this fundraising postcard mistakenly identifies the *U-58* as an American submarine. (Ian Lawler Collection)

OFFICIAL WAR POSTAL CARD

PHOTO COPYRIGHT BY COMMITTEE ON PUBLIC INFORMATION

100

AN AMERICAN SUBMARINE IN ACTION.

Englands Not.

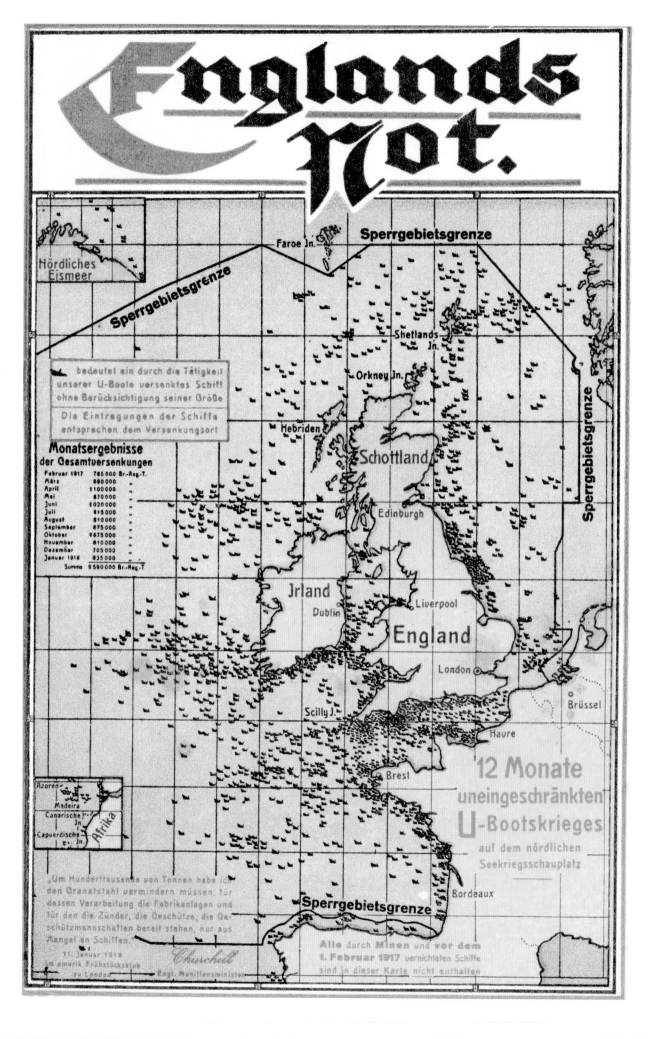

coast of Scotland, following a wireless communication with Malin Head, Co. Donegal, the *Viknor* went missing and was presumed lost. It was later determined that she struck one of the mines that had been laid earlier by the former German liner, the *Berlin*. There were no survivors of this sinking; the bodies of many of the 294 crew and passengers washed ashore on the north coast of Ireland.

Another notable wartime loss occurred on 21 April 1916, when German naval personnel scuttled one of their own ships in Irish coastal waters. Disguised as a Norwegian merchant ship, a German vessel, the *Aud*, was packed with a large cargo of arms and munitions destined for Irish republicans in the run-up to a planned rebellion that Easter (24–30 April). Sailing from Germany through the North Sea, around Scotland, the *Aud* had managed to evade British naval patrols, and proceeded down the west coast of Ireland unmolested. The vessel was supposed to rendezvous with a German submarine, *U-19*, off the Magharee Islands, Co. Kerry. On board *U-19* was the former British diplomat and Irish nationalist, Roger Casement, whose role was to supervise the delivery and distribution of the cargo to fellow rebels. Instead, after failing to meet with *U-19* as planned, the *Aud*'s suspicious movements along the coastline attracted attention and she was detained by the British Navy. While being escorted to Cobh (then Queenstown), Co. Cork, she was scuttled by her German crew, just outside the entrance to Cork harbour. British Navy divers and other divers hired locally in Cork completed an extensive salvage of the *Aud*, recovering some of the illicit cargo. These findings allowed for a successful prosecution against the main conspirator, Roger Casement.

At the time, the naval facilities at Cobh, under the command of Admiral Lewis Bayly, became the centre of operations for clearing the submarine threat from Irish waters. By the end of 1916 the fleet in the Cork port would be comprised of 15 Q-ships, 12 sloops, 23 armed steam trawlers, nine drifters, four armed steam yachts, 12 motor launches and four old torpedo boats. Later, when America entered the war, these were supplemented by an extensive American naval presence, with Berehaven in Bantry Bay becoming an important naval base for both the British Navy and the American Navy. From 1917 American destroyers, cruisers, submarines and anti-submarine boats patrolled the southern approaches to Ireland, escorting inbound transatlantic convoys to safety. One of the greatest

Opposite: German propaganda postcard celebrating the sinking of almost 10,000,000 tons of allied shipping during a 12-month period from February 1917 to January 1918 in the zone of unrestricted submarine warfare in waters around Ireland, Britain and France. (Ian Lawler Collection)

successes of the US Navy in World War I was the capture of *U-58* off Cork in November 1917 by USS *Fanning* and USS *Nicholson*. Although the crew of the U-boat managed to scuttle the vessel before the Americans could take control of it, the crew were captured and the incident was regarded as a major success: the first sinking of an enemy submarine in US naval history (see p.87 for more details).

As 1916 drew to a close, the Lords of the Admiralty had some reason to feel relieved. The rate of vessels being sunk in the Irish Channel had been decreasing and fears that the rebellion in Ireland would threaten Britain's military and economic interests had abated. Following something of a reprieve in 1916, the German submarines renewed their offensive on 1 February 1917, with the declaration of a second 'unrestricted U-boat campaign'. This was the declared date of commencement, but attacks of this nature had already begun in January. The German submarine *U-80* laid mines off the coast of Donegal, on the approach to Lough Swilly, to hinder access to the large British naval base established there. At the time, large shipments of gold were being transported to America in order to pay for valuable war material that the British urgently required to maintain their armies on various fronts, including Belgium and France. The former White Star liner *Laurentic*, displacing 14,892 tons and later commissioned as an armed merchant cruiser, was specially chosen to transport £5 million in gold bars to the Canadian port of Halifax, departing Liverpool on 24 January 1917. On the following day the vessel called into Lough Swilly en route, in order to avoid potential submarine attack during daylight hours as well to disembark some naval personnel at Buncrana, Co. Donegal. As the light faded, the *Laurentic* made its way out into the open ocean. The vessel struck one or two mines laid by *U-80* and sank in 45 minutes, taking her precious cargo with her. There were 475 men on board, and 354 died either in the mine explosions or in the freezing water. The Royal Navy began a marathon salvage project, which lasted until 1924 and recovered 3,186 of the 3,211 bars of gold the *Laurentic* was carrying.

Heavy losses were experienced in Irish waters during the spring of 1917, followed by a short-lived decline and then later resurgence for the remainder of 1917. The Germans believed that if U-boats could attain and maintain sinkings of 600,000 tons per month, then Britain would be starved of vital overseas supplies and would be forced to surrender. In February, 540,000 tons of shipping was sunk, followed by 603,000 tons in March. Given the trend, it was estimated by the Admiralty that Britain would be defeated before the end of November 1917. The

Above: Painting by German artist Willy Stöwer (1864–1931) of a U-boat sinking a French sailing ship. (Ian Lawler Collection)

U-boat commanders, such as Otto Steinbrinck in *UC-65* and Johannes Lohs in *UC-75*, appeared to operate quite freely in the Irish Channel. Steinbrinck managed to sink 18 vessels in the Irish Channel between 24 and 28 March, while during ten months of service the *UC-65* sank 115 vessels in total, before it was itself torpedoed by a British submarine in November 1917.

An unusual attack took place in Irish waters that year. On 28 March the South Arklow light vessel, *Guillemot*, was boarded by a crew from the German mine-laying submarine *UC-65*, who placed bombs in the bottom of the light vessel. After her crew took to the lifeboat, the bombs exploded, but the stoutly built vessel did not sink. She was then shelled by the U-boat's deck gun, before eventually sinking. This was the only light vessel to be purposely sunk in either of the world wars. The U-boat crew accused those aboard the *Guillemot* of warning passing vessels that an enemy submarine was in the area. This understandable action by the crew of the *Guillemot* was apparently outside the scope of an agreement on neutral status under which the light vessels had agreed to operate. One such

vessel warned by the light-keepers was the *Wychwood*, but it was sunk in any event. Both vessels are dived today by scuba divers and apart from the holes that sunk her, the *Guillemot*'s stout hull remains intact. The action was controversial, but the German accusation was not a false one as British and Irish light vessels had previously been involved in such contraventions of the rules of engagement.

Due to persistent attacks on American shipping in the Atlantic Ocean, including the *Lusitania* tragedy, America finally entered the war in April 1917. The reason behind the decision to enter the war has been the cause of much speculation ever since, but at that juncture America was quickly coming to the view that Britain, France and her allies were in real danger of defeat. Germany was under no illusion that, given enough time, the entry of this industrial giant would ultimately decide the outcome of the war. Every effort was now made to prevent the flood of American men and materials into the Western Front before Germany's spring offensive in 1918. Accordingly, the U-boats focused their attention on the western approaches to the coast of Ireland, so as to inhibit the build-up of American military might. A particular choke-point was off the north coast of Ireland and the North Channel, where many of the large troop and munitions carriers were ambushed. It was here that early attempts at 'wolf pack' tactics (*rudeltaktik*) were attempted by the German submarine commanders, but their efforts were in vain. By the spring, America had opened direct transatlantic routes to the west coast of France, where it landed thousands of troops to relieve the over-stretched British and French armies, although not before many more vessels were sunk and hundreds of lives lost around the coast of Ireland. The huge liner *Justicia*, en route from Belfast to America, was attacked by at least three submarines: *U-54*, *UB-64* and *UB-124*. The attack began on 19 July and ceased the following day, when the vessel was sunk (*see* p.103). This magnificent liner was one of many troop transports that were attacked and sunk in the approaches to Britain and Ireland in 1918, in a desperate attempt by U-boats and their crews to give their comrades-in-arms on the battlefields in France an opportunity for victory.

As the summer passed, victory was in the grasp of the Allies and desperation crept into the actions of the U-boat fleet. This desperation culminated in the worst tragedy ever to befall an Irish ship. The mail-boat run between Dún Laoghaire and Holyhead, an important lifeline for Ireland, was not suspended with the outbreak of war. If anything, the City of Dublin Steam Packet Company increased services, having four modern vessels in operation, each named after an Irish province: RMS *Ulster*, RMS *Munster*, RMS *Leinster* (*see* p.111) and RMS *Connaught*. These modern vessels attained speeds considered beyond the reach of the U-boats, a view that prevailed until March 1917, when the *Connaught*, after being requisitioned as a troop transport, was sunk by a U-boat in the English Channel. Apart from being provided with an escort from time to time, nothing else changed for her sister ships in the Irish Sea.

On the morning of 10 October the *Leinster* was sunk by *UB-123*, just 12 miles from her berth at Dún Laoghaire. The submarine fired three torpedoes, one passing across her bow, the second striking her on the port side and the third on her starboard side after she had turned in an attempt at returning to harbour. Over 500 lives were lost in the tragedy, the majority being military personnel. Ironically, *UB-123* and her crew did not survive much longer themselves as the submarine was lost in a minefield on its return trip to Germany. A month later an armistice

was agreed and the subsequent truce brought to an end a conflict that had inflicted much death and destruction in Ireland's coastal waters.

Throughout the war numerous other Irish vessels were attacked and sunk, with significant loss of life, due to belligerent actions. The City of Cork Steam Packet Company suffered badly during the war and provides a graphic illustration of the misfortune that befell so many ships and boats. Six of that company's cargo steamers — *Inniscarra*, *Innisfallen*, *Ardmore*, *Lismore*, *Kenmare* and *Bandon* — were attacked without warning by German U-boats. In all, 119 lives were lost during these attacks, which must have had tragic consequences for the numerous families affected by these dreadful events. Fishing vessels were not excluded from attack either. The *St. Michan* and the *Geraldine* (all lives lost) were sunk off Lambay Island in March 1918, while the *W.M. Barkley* and the SS *Adela* represent some of the Irish merchant ships sunk by U-boat action. The Guinness-owned *W.M. Barkley* (*see* p.86) was torpedoed without warning off Dublin in October 1917 with the loss of four lives, including the master, while the SS *Adela* was similarly torpedoed en route from Dublin to Liverpool with the loss of 24 lives. The loss of Irish lives during the war, both in trenches on the Continent and at sea, was enormous. It is estimated that over 30,000 Irish men and women died, which obviously had a lasting impact on Irish society for generations to come. The German Navy suffered, too, with 15 of the 178 German U-boats sunk during World War I being lost in Irish waters. A number of these U-boats have now been located and surveyed, including the *U-89* off Donegal (*see* p.92) and the *UC-42* (*see* p.83) and the *U-58* (*see* p.87) off the coast of Cork.

As technology improves and these wrecks become more accessible and real to the casual observer, they have the capacity to bring the events of those times back to life in a way that puts us in direct contact with history. Yet we can only begin to imagine the terror experienced by those whose lives were put at risk or lost when caught up in the horrific events of the time. As such, these wreck sites should be preserved for future generations in the hope that they will look back and affirm, 'never again', while perhaps marvelling at the sophistication and even the beauty of some of these wartime vessels.

Following pages: The sheer scale of the 1,164-ton *U-118* can be appreciated as it stands on the beach at Hastings, England. The submarine drifted ashore at Hastings after its tow cable broke while being transferred to Scapa Flow to be scrapped. It was broken up and scrapped at the end of 1919. (Ian Lawler Collection)

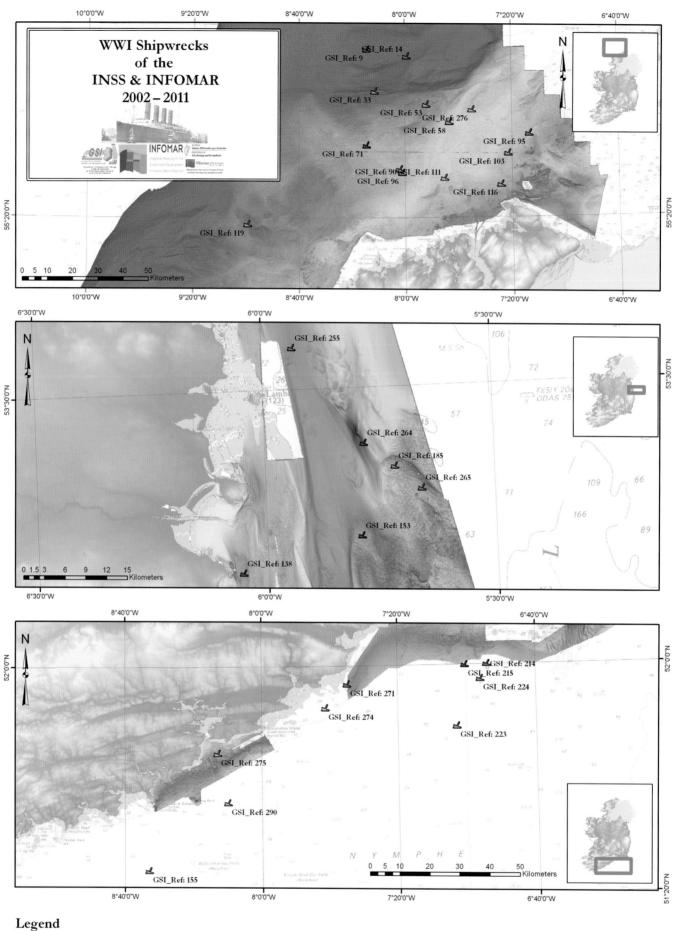

Legend

VESSEL TYPE

CARGO VESSEL	MERCHANT SHIP	PASSENGER LINER	RIGGED SHIP	SUBMARINE
BATTLESHIP	DRIFTER	OCEAN LINER	PASSENGER SHIP	STEAM COLLIER

Compiled and written by Karl Brady, Charise McKeon, James Lyttleton and Ian Lawler

HMS Audacious

GSI ref. code	111
NMS wreck no.	W07147
Location	24km WNW of Malin Head, Co. Donegal
Co-ordinates	55 28 17.26N, 007 45 7.52W
Depth of water	59.8m
Vessel type	Dreadnought Battleship
Vessel dimensions	182m (l), 27m (b), 8m (d)
Date of building	1913
Date of loss	27 October 1914

Circumstances of loss

The *Audacious*, a 23,000-ton, King George V class super-dreadnought battleship, was the first capital ship to be lost by any nation in World War I. It was the deadliest ship of its time, confidently considered to be unsinkable. It was built at Birkenhead in 1913 by Cammell, Laird & Co. Ltd and was equipped with ten 13.5-inch guns, sixteen 4-inch guns and four 3-pounders. It measured 182m in length and 27m

Below: Crew of the sinking *Audacious* take to the lifeboats before being rescued by a passing ship, the White Star liner *Olympic*. (Courtesy of the Imperial War Museum)

beam, and was capable of 22.4 knots. Under the command of Captain Cecil Frederick Dampier, this battleship was assigned to the 2nd Battle Squadron. At 8.45am on the morning of 27 October 1914, while manoeuvring to take part in target practice near Tory Island, the *Audacious* struck a mine – one of 200 mines laid across the main shipping route along Ireland's northern coastline by an armed liner, the Norddeutscher Lloyd's *Berlin*.

Despite severe damage, which caused the port side and centre engine room to flood, the vessel attempted to reach the Royal Navy's base at Lough Swilly. In rough seas, the *Audacious* became quite unmanageable and was approached by the White Star liner *Olympic* and taken in tow, but unfortunately the towline parted. A second attempt was made to tow the stricken *Audacious*, this time by the fleet collier *Thornhill* and the light cruiser *Liverpool*, but with the same result. The battleship *Exmouth* arrived on the scene after some time, but was too late to be of any assistance. By 5.00pm the stern of the *Audacious* was awash. At that stage most of the non-essential crew had been taken off safely by the *Olympic*. Subsequent attempts at towing the damaged vessel proved unsuccessful, and by 6.30pm Captain Dampier and the remaining officers had left the ship. At 8.45pm the vessel

capsized, floating keel up. Around 9.00pm there was a massive explosion near the bow of the ship, which caused the ship to sink immediately.

A dive expedition led by Innes McCartney in 2008 has suggested that the highly unstable propellant cordite, which was contained in Clarkson cases in the forward magazines, may have become unstable and ignited as the vessel sank, causing this second explosion. Regardless, it was the work of a German mine that had destroyed the 'unsinkable' battleship and it was a huge boost for the German war campaign. From a British point of view, the loss of one of the Royal Navy's most powerful ships in the early stages of the war was such a disaster for the British Admiralty that news of the calamity was stringently suppressed until the war was over.

On the seafloor

The *Audacious* is an enormous wreck, and while she now lies inverted on the seabed with much of the forward section of the hull missing, it is still possible to discern all of the salient features of this unique dreadnought vessel.

Above: The HMS *Audacious* being evacuated before sinking. Painting by William Lionel Wyllie (1851–1931), a noted maritime artist. (Courtesy of the National Maritime Museum, Greenwich)

The wreck stands 16m proud above a sandy seabed at a depth of 64m. It measures 112m in length, 27m in width and is orientated NW–SE on the seafloor. The hull of the wreck aft of the armoured conning tower is fairly intact, though starting to collapse, with gigantic 10-inch armour plates starting to peel away from the hull. Aft, the four gigantic high-speed screws with two paddle-shaped rudders make for an impressive scene. The most iconic sight of the wreck, however, is to be found forward of the main hull and comprises the inverted B turret, with two 15m long barrels of the 13.5-inch guns protruding along the seabed. The barrel rifling can be seen inside the muzzle and both the 635kg shells and the brass Clarkson cases, which held the cordite that was capable of propelling them over 20km, are strewn all around the area. The gutted remains of the A turret barbette are to starboard of B turret and a number of the 4-inch casement-mounted guns of the secondary

Above: High-resolution, 3D, multibeam view of the *Audacious*. The nearly obliterated remains of the bow, lying almost at right-angles to its starboard side, are clearly visible (*left*), as are the remains of the upturned gun turrets, conning tower and stern section of the vessel (*coloured red*), which stands 16m proud above the seabed. (Courtesy of www.deepsea.se)

armament can also be seen protruding from the wreckage around the conning tower. The bow was nearly obliterated by the explosion that occurred after she capsized and is now located at right-angles to the starboard side of the wreck, about 20m out from the conning tower and turrets. All that is left is a short piece of the stem and the starboard anchor and hawse. Some sediment scouring has occurred around the bow area of the wreck.

Above: A diver is dwarfed by the massive scale of the overturned gun turret with its pair of 13.5-inch guns. These once formed part of the considerable arsenal of weapons available to this super dreadnought battleship. (Photo Barry McGill)

Printed Sources

Bishop 2006, 16–21
Hepper 2006, 27–8
Hocking 1969, 60
McGill 2010, 74–7
UKHO Wreck Data

HMS Viknor

GSI ref. code	71
NMS wreck no.	W07837
Location	35km N of Tory Island, Co. Donegal
Co-ordinates	55 35 07.19N, 08 14 30.05W
Depth of water	83m
Vessel type	Passenger Liner / Armed Merchant Cruiser
Vessel dimensions	128m (l), 15m (b), 7.6m (d)
Date of building	1888
Date of loss	13 January 1915

Circumstances of loss

The *Viknor*, formerly known as the *Atrato*, was built in 1888 by Robert Napier & Miller in Govan, Glasgow, as a 5,386-ton passenger liner for the Royal Mail Steam Packet Company. The liner had triple-expansion engines that enabled speeds up to 14 knots. It operated as a passenger liner on the England–West Indies service for 24 years, until bought by the Viking Cruising Company in 1912 and renamed the *Viking*. In 1914 the vessel was requisitioned by the British Admiralty and converted into an auxiliary cruiser, renamed HMS *Viknor*. At the time of its loss, the *Viknor* was participating in a blockade patrol to the north of the Shetland Islands with the 10th Cruiser Squadron. After intercepting a Norwegian steamer, the SS *Bergensfjord*, carrying eight German passengers, the *Viknor* was ordered to transport the German prisoners to Liverpool. The following day, on 13 January 1915, the *Viknor* went missing north of Malin Head in very rough weather. It is possible that the cruiser sank as a result of the bad weather, but it is more likely that it sank as a result of striking a mine. This is suggested by the fact that it was last heard of in the vicinity of a recently laid German minefield. The vessel's Commander, Ernest Orford Ballantyne, the 22 officers, 273 ratings and eight German prisoners all drowned. Wreckage and bodies were washed ashore along the north coast of Ireland and the west coast of Scotland, with some of the victims buried at

Below: Photo of the 5,386-ton passenger liner as the *Atrato,* which operated on the England–West Indies service between 1888 and 1912. (Courtesy of the National Maritime Museum, Greenwich)

Above: Postcard of the liner as the *Viking* when it operated as a cruising steam yacht for the Viking Cruising Company from 1912 until it was requisitioned in 1914 for war service. (Ian Lawler Collection)

graveyards in Bonamargy and Ballintoy, Co. Antrim, and on Oronsay Island in the Hebrides.

On the seafloor

The wreck of the *Viknor* measures 124m in length, 28.5m in width and 2.1m in maximum height, with an average height of 1.8m. The vessel is orientated WNW–ESE on the seafloor and shows little relief in the multibeam sonar scan. The ravages of time have not been kind to the *Viknor* and there is very little left now that is recognisable as a ship. Despite this, the graceful clipper bow lying on its port side is easily recognisable, while aft the eight boilers and engine block, topped with the cold water coral *Lophelia*, lead to the remains of the stern, comprising the propeller, rudder and rudder quadrant. The 4.7-inch guns, probably eight in total, are scattered throughout the wreckage.

Above: The rudder and propeller are still evident amongst the jumbled wreckage of the HMS *Viknor*. (Photo Barry McGill)

Printed Sources

Hepper 2006, 31–2

Hocking 1969, 740

Larn & Larn 2002

Lusitania

Written by Fionnbarr Moore

GSI ref. code	155
NMS wreck no.	W08561
Location	22km S of Old Head of Kinsale, Co. Cork
Co-ordinates	51 24 44.71N, 008 32 52.19W
Depth of water	88m
Vessel type	Passenger Liner
Vessel dimensions	232m (l), 27m (b), 17m (d)
Gross tonnage	30,396 tons
Date of building	1907
Date of loss	7 May 1915

History and circumstances of loss

The 30,396-ton *Lusitania*, together with its sister ship, the *Mauritania*, was the pride of the Cunard Line when it was built in 1906. The liner was designed by the engineer Leonard Peskett and built by John Brown & Co. Ltd. of Glasgow. It was finished in June 1906 and fitted out for her maiden voyage to New York, which was scheduled for the following September. Its arrival in New York was a major event, with the ship receiving a rapturous welcome and hailed as the finest ship in the world. The building of

the *Lusitania* had stemmed from a low-interest loan given to the owners by the British government, which required fast Atlantic civilian liners capable of being pressed into naval service as auxiliary cruisers at a moment's notice. The ship was the largest ship ever built at the time, protected by high tensile steel plating, capable of travelling at 25 knots and with its important equipment located below the waterline, to protect it from shellfire during hostilities. Another innovation was the electric controls for steering, detecting fire and closing the watertight compartments, of which there were 175. Four giant steam-turbine engines were fitted instead of the usual reciprocating pistons – the first time a merchant ship had been fitted out in this way. Provision was also made for 12 revolving wheels or gun rings for six 6-inch guns, as well as a number of compartments that could be used as magazines to hold

Opposite: The bow of the *Lusitania*, pictured at the time of its launch. Its graceful silhouette is a testimony to the skills and talents that Scotland's ship-building yards could draw on. (Ian Lawler Collection)

Below: The *Lusitania* arriving in the Hudson River, New York, where she was greeted by hundreds of thousands of people and great fanfare after completing her maiden voyage from Liverpool in September 1907. The Statue of Liberty is visible in the background. (Courtesy of the National Maritime Museum, Greenwich)

S.S. "LUSITANIA" (TURBINE), largest vessel in the world, 787 feet long, 88 feet beam, 60 feet in depth, built by John Brown & Co., Ltd., Clydebank.

shell stockpiles. There were first-class cabins amidships and the ship was luxuriously fitted out, with the first-class dining room and smoking room decorated in the neo-classical style of the 18th century. The second- and third-class accommodation was also of a relatively high standard. In providing this comfort for its less well-off passengers, Cunard was recognising the importance of the large number of third-class passengers, in particular, who would make the one-way journey to America as emigrants, thus bolstering significantly the profits of the Company.

Despite these modifications to make the liner suitable for conversion to an auxiliary cruiser, when war broke out in 1914 plans to use the *Lusitania* as a naval vessel were shelved due to its enormous coal consumption. Having successfully made five return trips to New York from Liverpool following the outbreak of hostilities, the *Lusitania* was once again en route to Liverpool in May 1915, on her 101st Atlantic crossing. She was carrying 1,257 passengers and 702 crew. While fast liners, like the *Lusitania*, routinely carried munitions to Britain, in the opinion of the German government, the *Lusitania* was carrying contraband, in the sense of goods forbidden to be supplied by neutrals to those engaged in war. This is still a controversial issue as under regulations governing American shipping at the time, it was permissible for the *Lusitania* to be carrying what were termed small arms ammunition, non explosive in bulk. In this regard, the *Lusitania* carried 1,248 cases of 3.3-inch shrapnel shells (unfilled), 4,927 cases of rifle bullets with around 1,000 cartridges per case, 3,240 percussion fuses for 6-inch

Above: The 30,396-ton liner was considered to be not only the most luxurious ship of its time but also the largest. It made 202 transatlantic crossings during its eight years in service. (Ian Lawler Collection)

Opposite, top: The passenger liner was equipped with the most up-to-date and comfortable accommodation for first-class passengers, as illustrated in this postcard of the *Lusitania*'s elegantly decorated lounge. (Ian Lawler Collection)

Opposite, bottom: This postcard shows the *Lusitania*'s first-class library, which could be used by passengers to amuse themselves on the long transatlantic voyages. (Ian Lawler Collection)

shells and 46 tons of aluminium powder. Furthermore, on 30 April, shortly before sailing, 70 passengers and 200 tons of cargo were transferred from the *Queen Margaret* to the *Lusitania*, and part of the transferred cargo was ammunition. We know this because the archives of the Remington Arms Company include a letter that refers to the loading of 2,000 cases of small arms ammunition on to the *Queen Margaret*, and attached to this letter was a Cunard receipt for 2,000 cases of .303 ammunition, with the name *Queen Margaret* cancelled and *Lusitania* written across it. Again this has been a source of controversy over the years, but it was apparently common practice for a ship to embark on an abbreviated manifest and to supply a full one after leaving port. In the case of the *Lusitania* the complete manifest listed all the arms it was legally carrying and this information was in the public domain shortly after the sinking. One thing that cannot be disputed, however, is that these arms were destined for use in the British war effort.

The Lounge,
s.s. LUSITANIA.

Above: The sinking of the *Lusitania* by *UB-123*, with the loss of 1,198 lives, was one of the worst maritime tragedies of WWI. For days afterwards bodies washed ashore along the Cork coastline or were recovered by local fishing boats. The bodies were buried in mass graves in Old Church cemetery, Cobh. (Ian Lawler Collection)

Above: The sinking of the *Lusitania* in May 1915 provoked outrage in Britain and increased tensions between Germany and America, the latter a neutral power at the time. The printing of commemorative stamps stirred public sentiment in both Britain and abroad against Germany's policy of unrestricted submarine warfare. (Ian Lawler Collection)

The captain of the ill-fated liner, William J. Turner, was warned on approaching the Irish coast that there was submarine activity in the area. His actions in response to the warnings are still disputed, but it would seem to be the case that he had reduced the speed of the vessel from 21 knots (its maximum speed at the time) to 18 in the hope that he would catch the full tide on the way into Liverpool and not have to hang off the Liverpool coast in what he may have thought would have been a more vulnerable position. Whatever his reasons were for not dealing effectively with the more immediate threat off the Irish coast, on the afternoon of 7 May the liner was detected and attacked by *U-20* under the command of *Kapitänleutnant* Walther Schwieger. A single torpedo struck the ship either just under her bridge or just after it, on the starboard side. Another explosion followed, most likely, in the boiler room in the forward part of the ship. The *Lusitania* sank in 18 minutes. There was difficulty launching the 22 standard and 26 collapsible lifeboats, which cost valuable time. Trawlers and tugs in the area quickly came to the aid of the sinking vessel, but 1,198 lives were lost in the incident. There were 764 survivors of the torpedo attack, including Captain Turner. It is uncertain whether one or two torpedoes were fired: witnesses reported having heard two explosions, but the captain of *U-20* subsequently insisted that only one torpedo was fired. The exact cause of the second explosion is still very much a matter for debate. The Remington Company provided sworn evidence at the subsequent inquiry asserting that the cartridges were safe,

Above: Multibeam view of the once magnificent liner lying on its starboard side, slowly collapsing in on itself. It once stood 20m high, but natural decay, salvage operations and depth-charging have taken their toll and the vessel now has a maximum height of 14.7m above the seabed. It measures 241m long, 46m at its widest and has an average height of 9.9m

and Bethlehem Steel likewise maintained that its shells were not fitted with fuses or primed to explode on impact. Recent dives on the wreck have identified cases of .303 cartridges, but no evidence of an explosion in the storage area containing them.

The sinking of the *Lusitania* was celebrated in Germany, and was used by Britain and her allies as a means of exerting pressure on America to enter the war. Two public hearings followed: one chaired by Lord Mersey in Westminster, in 1915; a court hearing to settle the claims of the Cunard Company was convened by Judge Julius Mayer in New York in 1918. Since then the vessel has continued to attract much attention. In 1917 the Royal Navy examined the wreck, while others interested in the vessel for salvage purposes included the Liverpool & Glasgow Salvage Association, an American film crew in the 1930s and Captain Henry Russell of the *Orphir* in 1935. In 1954 the Royal Navy once again carried out investigations, followed by John Light in the early 1960s, Oceaneering International in 1982 and Robert Ballard in 1993. The ship's bell, lifted by Oceaneering, is on display in the Imperial War Museum in London. Oceaneering International also recovered three of the four 16-ton manganese bronze propellers, two of the ship's anchors, the ship's whistle, silver plate spoons, watch cases, 821 brass fulminate of mercury fuses for 6-inch shells, an unexploded depth charge from 1946, china, silver dishes, the foghorn and a telegraph. The items didn't make as much as anticipated in the subsequent Sotheby's auction,

as a result of which one of the propellers was melted down and converted into 3,500 golf clubs, to be sold for $9,000 a set; another propeller can be seen on the docks at Liverpool while the third is in Dallas. In 1995 the wreck was afforded protection by an Underwater Heritage Order and since then all activities and diving on the wreck have been subject to licensing by the National Monuments Service.

On the seafloor

The wreck of the *Lusitania* measures 241m in length, 46m in width and 14.7m in maximum height, with an average height of 9.9m. The vessel is orientated NE–SW on the seafloor, with its bow to the NE. The wreck lies on its starboard side, thus concealing the area where the torpedo struck the vessel. A combination of the violent nature of its sinking, several salvage operations, depth-charging by the Royal Navy in the late 1940s, the natural decaying processes and the ravages of the north Atlantic swell have all taken their toll on the remains of the vessel. The wreck is slowly deteriorating, collapsing in on itself. Most of the bulkheads and decks have collapsed and the hull is separated from the bulkheads in many places. A large debris field lies along the starboard side of the wreck. In spite of this ongoing decline, the bow still stands proud of the seabed and many of the structural features are still clearly discernible.

Printed Sources
Ballard 1995
Hocking 1969, 436-7
Larn & Larn 2002
Maloney 2004
Preston 2002
Simpson 1996

Folia

GSI ref. code	274
NMS wreck no.	W08274
Location	7km S of Ram Head, Co. Waterford
Co-ordinates	51 52 51.82N, 007 41 20.77W
Depth of water	30m
Vessel type	Ocean Liner
Vessel dimensions	132m (l), 16m (b), 7.6m (d)
Date of building	1907
Date of loss	11 March 1917

Above: A machinery wheel on the wreck of the *Folia*. (Photo Timmy Carey)

Circumstances of loss

The SS *Folia* was originally named the *Principe di Piemonte* when built in 1907 by Sir James Laing & Sons Ltd of Sunderland for the Lloyd Sabaudo Line of Genoa. She was one of three vessels that the Italian company ordered from Laing's for their Genoa–New York passenger service, the others being the *Re d'Italia* and the *Regina d'Italia*. The three sister ships were very similar in design, each possessing two masts and two funnels, except that the *Principe* had a slightly larger tonnage of 6,365 tons. Powered by 869 horsepower, six-cylinder, triple-expansion engines, the liner was capable of achieving 14 knots. In 1913 the Uranium Steamship Company purchased the vessel and renamed it *Principello*, sailing it between Rotterdam and New York. In 1914 the *Principello* was sold to the Canadian Northern's Royal Line and placed on the Canada–Avonmouth route. In 1916 she was bought by the Cunard Steamship Company and renamed the SS *Folia*. From 1916 until her loss the following year, the vessel was used as a cargo ship, plying between Liverpool and New York.

It was during one such voyage that the liner, under the command of Captain F. Inch, came to an unfortunate end when it was torpedoed, without warning, by German submarine *U-53*, under the command of *Kapitänleutnant* Hans Rose. The torpedo struck the steamer amidships on its port side, blowing two lifeboats into the air. With the *Folia* heavily loaded with general war supplies, including empty brass shell cases, she sank quickly, but the crew managed to launch the remaining lifeboats. The U-boat subsequently surfaced and fired four shells and a second torpedo to ensure the liner sank to the bottom of the sea. Seven lives were lost in total. The survivors made for the Waterford coast and landed in Ardmore Bay. The wreck was salvaged for brass in 1977.

Below: The wreck of the *Folia* lies on the edge of a small slope in an area dominated by rocky seabed.

Above: The SS *Folia*, originally named the *Principe di Piemonte*, pictured sometime between 1907 and 1913. During this period it was owned by the Lloyd Sabaudo Line of Genoa and operated on the Genoa–New York passenger service. (Ian Lawler Collection)

On the seafloor

The wreck of the SS *Folia* measures 113.2m long and is spread over an area 16.5m wide. It stands a maximum of 5.2m above the seafloor. The wreck was salvaged extensively by Risdon Beazley Marine Ltd, a salvage company, in 1977 for its cargo of brass, and as a result little remains that is recognisable as a ship. The bow is the one exception and forms the highlight of any dive. It lies in a general sea depth of 33m and is orientated almost E–W.

Above: Divers decompressing on a shot line after diving the *Folia*. (Photo Timmy Carey)

Printed Sources
BVLS 1914–18
Hocking 1969, 247
Larn & Larn 2002
Smith 1947, 88, 151, 152
Tennent 1990, 60

Internet Source
www.wrecksite.eu

Antony

GSI ref. code	215
NMS wreck no.	W03173
Location	14km SW of Hook Head, Co. Wexford
Co-ordinates	52 0 6.88N, 007 0 18.43W
Depth of water	57m
Vessel type	Passenger Liner
Vessel dimensions	127m (l), 16m (b), 8m (d)
Date of building	1907
Date of loss	17 March 1917

Circumstances of loss

In February 1917 Germany announced a second unrestricted phase of submarine warfare against Allied shipping. Submarine warfare became widespread off the coast of Ireland, resulting in significant numbers of shipping losses, including the loss of the liner *Antony*, with 55 lives. The *Antony* was a 6,446-ton, twin-screw steam liner owned by the Booth Line of Liverpool and was employed on the passenger and mail service that plied between Britain, Argentina and Brazil. It was launched in February 1907 by Hawthorn Leslie & Co., of Newcastle, at a cost of £123,000. It was capable of carrying 572 passengers and completed its maiden voyage from Britain to the Amazon in March of the same year. It measured over 127m in length and its triple-expansion engine delivered up to 14 knots in maximum speed. With the onset of war it was lightly armed with a stern-mounted 6-inch gun.

At the time of its loss, the *Antony* was under the command of Captain A.W. Stoker, travelling from Belém, in Brazil, to Liverpool with four passengers, 126 crewmen and a cargo of rubber. Unbeknownst to the *Antony*, the *UC-48* was patrolling the southeast coast of Ireland and without warning it torpedoed the liner on its port side, flooding the engine room and leaving the vessel helpless against further attacks. The *Antony* was abandoned immediately, but 55 lives were lost during the course of evacuation, with only 75 survivors eventually landed at Cobh, Co. Cork. The liner was torpedoed twice more and bombarded with several shells, causing it to catch fire and sink. The *Antony* was one of four vessels sunk over a two-day period off the Wexford and Waterford coasts by *UC-48*.

Below: The 'dining saloon' on board the *Antony*. (Ian Lawler Collection)

Above: Passengers on board liners often bought postcards of the ships they were travelling on to send home news of their safe arrival at their destination or to provide updates of their travels. This postcard shows the *Antony* under steam in tropical waters, possibly in the Amazon River, as suggested by the palm trees along the shoreline. (Ian Lawler Collection)

Above, top: This postcard shows the 'music room' on board the *Antony*. (Ian Lawler Collection)

Above, bottom: Multibeam image of the wreck of the *Antony* lying on the seabed. The violent nature of the *Antony's* sinking, along with subsequent salvage operations, has accelerated the rate at which the 133m long wreck is disintegrating.

On the seafloor

The wreck of the *Antony* measures 133m in length, 20m in width and 6m maximum height, with an average height of 2.2m. The vessel is orientated NNW–SSE on the seafloor. She appears to be partly buried and/or broken up as it was partially salvaged at some point, exposing some of its cargo of rubber. The *Antony* lies in two main pieces and many dives are needed on each piece to get one's bearings. She lies in 57m of water on one side, with her bilge keel facing up. Most of her triple-expansion steam engines stick out clear of the hull plating. Two of her five boilers can clearly be seen poking their way through tears in the hull's steelwork, wide enough for the adventurous diver to visit inside. What is most striking to the diver is the seemingly endless rows of round portholes studded along the almost horizontal hull plating when swimming down towards the small debris field between the wreck and the seabed.

Printed Sources

Hocking 1989, 38
Larn & Larn 2002
Roche 1993, 120, 131
Stokes 1996

UKHO Wreck Data 1996
Williams 1997, 46

Internet Source

www.uboat.net

SS Bandon

GSI ref. code	271
NMS wreck no.	W04769
Location	5km S of Mine Head, Co. Waterford
Co-ordinates	51 56 56.23N, 007 34 47.98W
Depth of water	33m
Vessel type	Cargo vessel
Vessel dimensions	81.1m (l), 11.3m (b), 5.2m (d)
Date of building	1910
Date of loss	13 April 1917

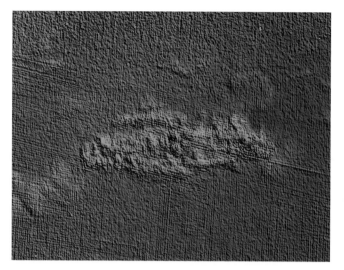

Above: A 3D, multibeam view of the wreck from the SW. The broken-up nature of the wreck makes it difficult to discern much detail in the multibeam data, but the two boilers (*coloured red*) are clearly discernible amidships.

Circumstances of loss

Built in 1910 by Swan, Hunter & Wigham Richardson Ltd. in Newcastle-upon-Tyne, the SS *Bandon* was owned by the City of Cork Steam Packet Company Ltd. Grossing 1,456 tons, the vessel was propelled by a 394 horsepower, three-cylinder, triple-expansion steam engine that provided speeds up to 14.5 knots. Given that the *Bandon* was plying her trade in dangerous times, the vessel was armed with one 3-pounder gun on the stern for defensive purposes. However, lightly armed merchant vessels could do little to fend off the menace of U-boats, which attacked without warning. The Cork Steam Packet Navigation Company suffered badly during World War I at the hands of U-boats, with the loss of six of its cargo steamers: *Inniscarra*, *Innisfallen*, *Ardmore*, *Lismore*, *Kenmare* and *Bandon*.

The SS *Bandon* was en route from Liverpool to Cork, under the command of Captain P.F. Kelly, when it was either torpedoed or mined by *UC-44* (*Kapitänleutnant* Kurt Tebbenjohanns) late on the afternoon of Friday, 13 April 1917. The torpedo struck the port side, disabling the engine room and causing the ship to sink immediately, 5km southwest of Mine Head. The 1,050-ton cargo was lost in the attack, along with 28 members of the crew. Only four crew members, including the ship's master,

were rescued by a motor launch sent by the Mine Head Lighthouse, after spending 2.5 hours in the water. They were landed at Dungarvan. The *UC-44* was responsible for sinking 29 other ships during World War I. Less than a year later, Captain P.F. Kelly survived another U-boat attack when the SS *Inniscarra*, which he was commanding, was torpedoed and sunk by *U-86* off the Waterford coast, once again with the loss of 28 lives.

On the seafloor

The wreck of the SS *Bandon* measures 81.9m in length, 11.5m in width and 5.5m in maximum height. The vessel is badly broken up and lies in a general sea depth of 33m and is orientated almost E–W, with its bow lying to the E.

Printed Sources
Barry 1919, 1–16
BVLS 1914–1918, 42
Hocking 1969, 69
Larn & Larn 2002
Tennent 1990, 44

Calchas

GSI ref. code	134
NMS wreck no.	W05584
Location	28km W of Valentia Island, off the coast of Co. Kerry
Co-ordinates	51 54 35.89N, 010 49 51.31W
Depth of water	126m
Vessel type	Cargo vessel
Vessel dimensions	135m (l), 16m (b), 9m (d)
Date of building	1899
Date of loss	11 May 1917

Circumstances of loss

The *Calchas* was a 6,748-ton steamship owned by the Liverpool-based Ocean Steam Ship Co. (Alfred Holt Group). It was built by Scott & Co. Ltd. of Greenock, Scotland, in 1899 at a cost of £83,983. The vessel had a single screw, was powered by a three-cylinder, triple-expansion engine and was armed with one 4.7-inch, stern-mounted gun. At the time of its loss the *Calchas* was under charter to the Cunard Line, bringing vital food supplies and 10,000 tons of munitions from New York to Liverpool for the war effort. It was attacked without warning by *U-80* (under the command of *Kapitänleutnant* Alfred von Glasenapp), with one torpedo striking the vessel's port side. It took an hour for the *Calchas* to sink, allowing plenty of time for Captain R.T. Jon and his 67 crew members to abandon the ship using four lifeboats. They were picked up soon afterwards by a naval ship and disembarked safely at Cobh, Co. Cork. The *Calchas* was one of two ships sunk on 11 May 1917 off the southwest coast of Ireland by *U-80*. Although it was reported at the time that the *Calchas* had sunk 5 miles west by south of Inistearaght Rocks, in the early 1950s the salvage company Risdon Beazley Marine Ltd located the wreck 28km west of Valentia Island. Approximately 269 tons of nickel was salvaged in 1954 and 1957.

On the seafloor

The wreck of the *Calchas* measures 72m in length, 23m in width and 7.9m in maximum height, with an average height of 5m. The vessel is orientated NE–SW on the seafloor. A deep sediment scour has developed at the NE end of the vessel.

Printed Sources

Halkett 2006, 148

Larn & Larn 2002

New York Times, 21 May 1917

Tennent 1990, 131

UKHO Wreck Data 1996

Internet Source

www.uboat.net

Above: German propaganda postcard celebrating the sinking of 781,500 tons of allied shipping during February 1917. The SS *Calchas* was one such vessel lost during 1917. It was bringing essential food supplies and munitions from America to Britain for the war effort when it was torpedoed off the Kerry coast. (Ian Lawler Collection)

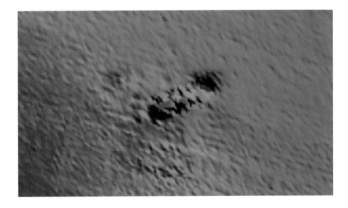

Above: Multibeam overview of the 72m long wreck in deep water, 28km west of Valentia Island. A significant sediment scour has developed at the NE end of the vessel.

Saint Mirren

GSI ref. code	9
NMS wreck no.	W07586
Location	79km NW of Malin Head, Co. Donegal
Co-ordinates	55 54 53.86N, 008 14 19.46W
Depth of water	178m
Vessel type	Full-rigged ship
Vessel dimensions	83m (l), 12m (b), 7m (d)
Date of building	1892
Date of loss	26 May 1917

Circumstances of loss

The *Saint Mirren* was a 1,956-ton, three-masted steel ship built by the Scottish shipbuilders Charles Connell & Company in 1892. It was initially owned by A. Mackey & Co., Glasgow, though at the time of its loss it was owned by Robert Thomas & Co., Liverpool, while being operated by Ship Conway Castle Co. Ltd. The vessel was lost while en route from the Clyde to Santos in Sao Paulo, under Captain J. Williams, with a 3,262-ton cargo of coal and patent fuel. It was attacked by *U-87* (under the command of *Kapitänleutnant* Rudolf Schneider), forcing the crew to abandon the ship. The *U-87* then sank the *Saint Mirren* by firing shells from its deck gun. The crew were rescued the next day by the SS *Ebro* and brought to Glasgow.

On the seafloor

The wreck of the *Saint Mirren* measures 90m in length, 21m in width and 7.6m in maximum height, with an average height of 4.1m. The vessel is orientated NW–SE, and a slight scour has developed in the seafloor around the vessel. There are clear upward protrusions at the bow and stern of the wreck.

Printed Sources
BVLS 1914–1918, 51
Larn & Larn 2002

Internet Source
www.clydesite.co.uk

Below: The 1,956-ton, steel, three-masted ship under full sail, pictured shortly after it was launched in 1892. (Courtesy of the National Maritime Museum, Greenwich)

Carthaginian

Above: Iconic view of the bow of the *Carthaginian* lying on the seabed in 54m of water. (Photo Barry McGill)

GSI ref. code	116
NMS wreck no.	W07211
Location	7km N of Malin Head, Co. Donegal
Co-ordinates	55 26 54.02N, 007 24 03.60W
Depth of water	54m
Vessel type	Passenger Liner
Vessel dimensions	117.6m (l), 13.7m (b)
Date of building	1884
Date of loss	14 June 1917

Circumstances of loss

The *Carthaginian* was a 4,444-ton steel steamship owned by the Allan Line Steamship Co. Ltd. of Govan, Glasgow. The vessel was built in 1884 by Govan Shipbuilding Co. Ltd. It was propelled by a 475 horsepower, compound steam engine and capable of attaining 14 knots in speed. The *Carthaginian* had a crew of 57, under the command of Captain A. Ogilvie, and could carry 596 passengers in three classes. Before the outbreak of hostilities in 1914 the vessel plied various transatlantic routes, typically out of Glasgow. She was subsequently armed with a 4-inch stern gun. On 14 June 1917, while on a voyage from the Clyde to Montreal with general cargo, she struck a mine 2.5 miles northwest of Inishtrahull, Co. Donegal, laid by *U-79* under the command of *Kapitänleutnant* Otto Rohrbeck. She sank, with the loss of 32 lives; the survivors were picked up by a British naval vessel and brought ashore at Buncrana, Co. Donegal. The *Carthaginian* was one of 22 ships sunk by *U-79* during 11 patrols. The HMT *Corientes* and HMT *Charles Astie* were also mined just north of Malin Head in June 1917 by the same U-boat. The *U-79* survived the war, surrendering to the French on 21 November 1918. It was subsequently used by the French Navy until 1935.

On the seafloor

The wreck of the *Carthaginian* is orientated NNW–SSE on the seabed and measures 116m in length, 21m in width and 4.3m in maximum height, with an average height of 2.1m. Although it is well broken up, there is still plenty to see on this wreck. The defensive stern gun can be found beside the rudder quadrant, along with the boilers and engine amidships. The bow is fairly upright, though it is now raked aft as the structure behind has collapsed, and the anchor derrick still stands on the fo'c'sle deck.

Printed Sources
BVLS 1914–1918, 55
Larn & Larn 2002
Tennent 1990, 37
Williams 1997, 56

Internet Source
www.uboat.net

Karina

GSI ref. code	223
NMS wreck no.	W03818
Location	34km SW of Hook Head, Co. Wexford
Co-ordinates	51 49 28.92N, 007 02 49.92W
Depth of water	73m
Vessel type	Passenger Liner
Vessel dimensions	112.8m (l), 14m (b), 7m (d)
Date of building	1905
Date of loss	1 August 1917

Circumstances of loss

The *Karina* was a 4,222-ton steamship built by Alexander Stephen & Sons, Linthouse, Glasgow, in 1905 and was employed on the Glasgow and Liverpool service to West Africa. It was one of two 'Karina' class steamships owned by the African Steam Navigation Company (Elder Dempster & Co. Ltd.), the other being the SS *Mendi*.

Both vessels were lost during the war: the *Karina* with the loss of 11 lives; the *Mendi* with the loss of 646 crew and passengers, mostly personnel from the South African Native Labour Corp, after being accidentally rammed by the SS *Darro* off the Isle of Wight. The *Karina*'s triple-expansion engines produced 422 horsepower, making it capable of speeds up to 12.5 knots. It had a 3-inch, stern-mounted gun for defensive purposes. On 30 July the *Karina* narrowly escaped being torpedoed during a U-boat attack off the west coast of Ireland, whilst en route from Sierra Leone to Liverpool with a 2,000-ton cargo of palm oil and palm kernels. Captain J.C. Hannay must have felt blessed to have had such a lucky escape, but his luck ran out just two days later when *UC-75*, under the command of *Oberleutnant zur See* Johannes Lohs, torpedoed the vessel without warning, hitting the no. 3 hold towards

Below: Postcard of the *Karina* painted in its African Steam Navigation Company livery, with a black hull, red waterline and black funnel. (Ian Lawler Collection)

R. M. S. Karina.

Weekly Sailings to
CANARY ISLANDS
WEST &
SOUTH WEST AFRICA

R.M.S. KARINA

ELDER DEMPSTER & CO LTD.
COLONIAL HOUSE, LIVERPOOL.

ARTISTIC
ALTRINCHAM

the aft of the ship. The *Karina* began to sink quickly and even though all six boats on board were launched, four passengers and seven crewmen drowned.

On the seafloor

The wreck of the *Karina* measures 106m in length and 28m in width, with an average height of 2.7m. The vessel is orientated NW–SE on the seafloor and appears to be partly buried, but three of its boilers stand 5.9m above the seabed. In 1985 the recovery of the ship's bell by Seasalve Marine confirmed the wreck to be the *Karina*.

Printed Sources

Anon. 2007
Hocking 1969, 373
Larn & Larn 2002
Tennent 1990, 71
UKHO Wreck Data 1996

Internet Source

www.theshiplist.com

Above: Postcard advertising the Elder Dempster & Co. Ltd.'s weekly service from Glasgow and Liverpool to West Africa on board the *Karina*. The 4,222-ton liner could carry 100 first-class passengers and 70 second-class passengers. (Ian Lawler Collection)

Below: A 3D, multibeam view of the *Karina*. Three of its boilers, standing almost 6m above the surrounding seabed, represent the highest part of the wreck, as indicated by the red areas in the image.

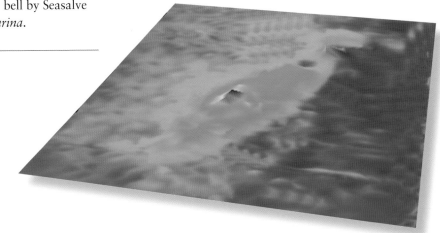

Athenia

GSI ref. code	103
NMS wreck no.	W07145
Location	15km NW of Inishtrahull Island, Co. Donegal
Co-ordinates	55 33 19.19N, 007 21 20.81W
Depth of water	54m
Vessel type	Passenger Liner
Vessel dimensions	146m (l), 17m (b), 10m (d)
Date of building	1904
Date of loss	16 August 1917

Circumstances of loss

The *Athenia* was an 8,668-ton, twin-screw British liner built by Vickers Sons & Maxim, Barrow-in-Furness, Cumbria, and owned by the Anchor-Donaldson Line. It had two decks, one funnel, four masts and triple-expansion engines. The liner was capable of reaching 13.5 knots and operated on the transatlantic passenger service between Glasgow and Canada. It was originally built as a cargo ship, but was converted to a liner in 1905. The *Athenia* was considered to be one of the first proper 'cabin' liners on the transatlantic trade, having accommodation for 50 first-class, 200 second-class and 1,000 third-class passengers.

At the time of its loss the liner was en route from Montreal to Glasgow, carrying 7,000 tons of general cargo, including empty shell cases, 440 horses, 109 passengers and 44 military personnel. Without warning, the *Athenia* was torpedoed by *U-53*, which was patrolling the waters off the north Donegal coast under the command of *Kapitänleutnant* Hans Rose. The *U-53* had already sunk 50 ships since 1916; it would sink 98 ships in total during the war years. The liner did not sink immediately, which enabled most of the crew and

Below: Painting of the *Athenia* under steam by F.F. Brichta. The *Athenia* was considered one of the first proper 'cabin' liners on the transatlantic trade, having accommodation for 50 first-class, 200 second-class and 1,000 third-class passengers. (Courtesy of the British Mercantile Marine Memorial Collection)

passengers to safely board the lifeboats. Two lifeboats made it to Inishtrahull Island, with some of the crew being saved by destroyers responding to *Athenia*'s SOS call. Sadly, however, 15 lives were lost during the attack.

The *U-53* continued to wreak carnage in the area over the coming days, sinking six more vessels, including the *Roscommon*, the *Devonian*, the *Boniface* and the *Kenmore*, with the lost of eight more lives and over 36,000 tons of shipping. The wreck of the *Athenia* was located by the salvage company Risdon Beazley Marine Ltd. in 1970 and was partially salvaged in 1975, with the recovery of 109 tons of brass.

On the seafloor
The wreck of the *Athenia* is orientated WNW–ESE on the seafloor. It is mostly buried, with the main protrusion from the seafloor being amidships. It measures 148m in length and has a maximum width of 43m. In 1974 the wreck stood 15m proud of the seabed, but in 2011 it had a maximum height of 10.6m, with an average height of 2.5m. The *Athenia* is another wreck that has been heavily salvaged, but in spite of this, it remains one of the most scenic wrecks in this depth range. The bow, now somewhat skeletal around the gunwales, but all the more picturesque for that, lies on its starboard side and the sand-polished brass letters 'ATH' of the vessel's name are visible on the seabed nearby. Aft the forehold has been torn open to get at the cargo of empty shell cases, many of which still lie strewn around on the seabed. Amidships the port side of the hull has toppled over onto the boilers, forming the highest point of the wreck, and aft further salvage work leads to the rudder quadrant and the defensive stern gun.

Printed Sources
Bonsor 1979, Vol. iii, 344–5
Halkett 2006, 148
Hocking 1969, 56
Larn & Larn 2002
UKHO Wreck Data 1996
Williams 1997, 60

Internet Source
www.uboat.net

Below: A 3D, multibeam image of the *Athenia*. The wreck measures 148m in length and is largely buried, with the main protrusion from the seafloor being amidships where the boilers stand. It is in poor condition in places as a result of the salvage work carried out in the 1970s.

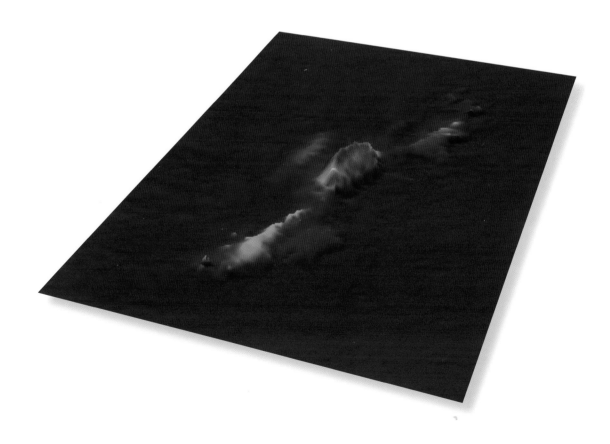

SS Devonian

GSI ref. code	90
NMS wreck no.	W07252
Location	44km NW of Malin Head, Co. Donegal
Co-ordinates	55 30 09.50N, 008 01 51.82W
Depth of water	75m
Vessel type	Passenger Liner
Vessel dimensions	168m (l), 18m (b), 11m (d)
Date of building	1900
Date of loss	21 August 1917

Circumstances of loss

The *Devonian* was a 10,418-ton steel steamship operated by the Leyland Line of Liverpool. The vessel was built by the famous Harland and Wolff shipyard in Belfast in 1900. It was propelled by an 847 horsepower, three-cylinder, triple-expansion engine, making it capable of attaining 14 knots in speed. It had a crew of 203 and carried up to 135 first-class passengers, serving the Liverpool–Boston route. The *Devonian* is probably best known for the role it played in the rescue of passengers of the passenger line *Volturno*, which caught fire and sank in the mid-Atlantic in October 1913, with the loss of 134 of the 654 passengers and crew on board. The *Devonian* was one of ten vessels that came to the *Volturno*'s assistance, saving 59 passengers and crew.

Following the outbreak of hostilities, the *Devonian* was lightly armed with a single 4.7-inch stern gun, but that offered little protection in the face of U-boat attack. On 21 August 1917, while in a westward-bound convoy and carrying only two passengers, she was torpedoed by

Below: Multibeam overview image of the *Devonian* on the seabed. The 170m long wreck lies 1.7km NW of the wreck of the *Roscommon*, which was also torpedoed by the *U-53* approximately 44km NW of Malin Head on 21 August 1917.

U-53, commanded by *Kapitänleutnant* Hans Rose. One lifeboat was destroyed in the explosion, but the remaining eight were lowered, allowing most of the crew to escape the sinking vessel. She sank 44km northeast of Tory Island, due north of Bloody Foreland, Co. Donegal, with the loss of two crew and 500 tons of general cargo. The survivors were rescued by a tug and trawler and taken to Lough Swilly, where they were landed safely at Buncrana, Co. Donegal.

On the seafloor

The wreck of the *Devonian* measures 170m in length, 28m in width and 6.1m in maximum height, with an average height of 1.9m.

Printed Sources
Hocking 1989, 187
Larn & Larn 2002
Tennent 1990, 154
Williams 1997, 60–61

Internet Source
www.uboat.net

Below: The 4.7-inch stern gun of the *Devonian* lying on the seabed. (Photo Barry McGill)

SS Roscommon

GSI ref. code	96
NMS wreck no.	W07575
Location	28km NE of Tory Island, off Co. Donegal
Co-ordinates	55 29 24.25N, 008 1 2.06W
Depth of water	73m
Vessel type	Cargo vessel
Vessel dimensions	137m (l), 17m (b), 12m (d)
Date of building	1902
Date of loss	21 August 1917

Circumstances of loss

The *Roscommon*, formerly known as the *Oswestry Grange*, was an 8,238-ton steel steamship of London, owned by the Union Steam Ship Company of New Zealand Ltd. The vessel was built in 1902 by Workman, Clark & Co. Ltd., Belfast, for Houlders Bros. & Co. The *Roscommon* was powered by two six-cylinder, triple-expansion engines with 662 horsepower and it carried a crew of 73 under the command of Captain A. Robertson. With the outbreak of hostilities, it was armed with a 4.7-inch stern gun.

On 21 August 1917 the *Roscommon* was torpedoed without warning by *U-53*, under the command of *Kapitänleutnant* Hans Rose, while on a voyage carrying cargo from Manchester to Australia. She was part of a convoy steaming at 7 knots when struck by a torpedo at 11.20am. It was initially thought that two of the crew drowned while taking to the boat, but it was later revealed that they were only injured. The vessel sank at midday and the survivors were taken by naval patrol vessels to Buncrana, Co. Donegal.

Below: Photo of the 8,238-ton steel cargo steamship as the *Oswestry Grange*, docked along the quayside. (Courtesy of the Museum of New Zealand Te Papa Tongarewa)

On the seafloor

The wreck of the *Roscommon* measures 132m in length, 26m in width, with an average height of 2.4m. The vessel is orientated ENE–WSW on the seafloor. Outward bound for the Antipodes, it is the cargo the *Roscommon* was carrying that makes her an interesting dive as, aside from the bow and boilers, there is little recognisable left of this ship. An eclectic collection of goods made in northeast England can be found at the wreck site, including crockery, stoneware crocks now devoid of their contents, panes of glass, decorative ceramic tiles for shopfronts and even a number of enormous millstones. Some luxury goods are also in evidence, as suggested by what appear to be champagne and burgundy bottles. A few of these can be found with their corks at least partially intact, but while the contents might still fizz on opening, they are always sulphurous and foul-smelling.

Above: The detached bow of the SS *Roscommon* on the seabed forms an impressive sight at 73m below the water surface. (Photo Barry McGill)

Above: Multibeam image of the SS *Roscommon*.

Opposite: Painting by James Bell of the SS *Oswestry Grange* sometime between 1902 and 1912, when it was owned by the Oswestry Grange Company of Greenock. (Courtesy of the British Mercantile Marine Memorial Collection)

Printed Sources
Anon. 2004
Larn & Larn 2002
McGill 2010, 74-7

Tennent 1990, 226
UKHO Wreck Data

Internet Source
www.uboat.net

Cooroy

GSI ref. code	224
NMS wreck no.	W03357
Location	18km S of Hook Head, Co. Wexford
Co-ordinates	51 57 37.84N, 006 55 57.43W
Vessel type	Merchant ship
Depth of water	62m
Vessel dimensions	93m (l), 13m (b), 7m (d)
Date of building	1892
Date of loss	29 August 1917

Circumstances of loss

The *Cooroy* was a 2,470-ton, four-masted steel barque. It was originally called the *Conishead*, when built in 1892 by R. Williamson of Workington. It was one of six four-masted barques known collectively as the 'Six Sisters' or the 'Workington Sisters', and was named after Conishead Priory in south Cumbria. It was originally owned by Bourke & Huntrods of Workington, but was sold to Reederei B. Wencke & Söhne of Hamburg in August 1898 and renamed *Athene*. In 1906 it was sold to another Hamburg shipping company, Rhederei Akt. Gesellschaft von 1896, staying in their ownership until it was interned by the Australian government at the start of World War I. In May 1915 it was chartered by Scott, Fell & Co. of London and renamed the *Cooroy*. The vessel, with a crew of 23, departed Tocopilla, Chile, bound for Liverpool with a cargo of nitrate. On the morning of 29 August 1917 the vessel was sighted and attacked with gunfire by *UC-75*, which was patrolling the southern approaches to St George's Channel. The *Cooroy* was immediately abandoned by its crew, who were rescued by the SS *Glengariff* and landed safely at Cobh, Co. Cork. An armed guard from the sloop HMS *Jessamine* boarded the *Cooroy* in an attempt to bring it ashore, but *UC-75* was still in the area and fired the torpedo that finally sunk the ship, killing all seven of the *Jessamine*'s boarding group.

On the seafloor

The wreck of the *Cooroy* measures 60m in length, 10m in width and 2.5m in maximum height, with an average height of 1.4m. The vessel is orientated NNW–SSE on the seafloor and appears to be mostly buried.

Printed Sources
Larn & Larn 2002
UKHO Wreck Data 1996

Internet Sources
www.bruzelius.info
www.mightyseas.co.uk
www.naval-history.net

Below: Photo of the newly launched, four-masted, steel barque *Conishead* at anchor in 1892. It was owned by Bourke & Huntrods of Workington at the time the photo was taken, renamed *Cooroy* in May 1915 after being chartered by Scott, Fell & Co. of London. (Courtesy of the National Maritime Museum, Greenwich)

UC-42

GSI ref. code	275
NMS wreck no.	W05519
Location	5.25km SE of Roches Point, Co. Cork
Co-ordinates	51 45 12.909N, 008 12 54.54W
Depth of water	27m
Vessel type	U-boat
Vessel dimensions	51m (l), 5m (b), 3.7m (d)
Date of building	21 September 1916
Date of loss	10 September 1917

Circumstances of loss

UC-42 is one of approximately 15 submarines sunk off the coast of Ireland during World War I. The submarine was built in the A.G. Vulcan shipyard in Hamburg and commissioned into service on 18 November 1916. It belonged to the UCII class of German U-boats: submarines that could attain a surface speed of 11.7 knots and cover a surface range of 9,410 nautical miles. These submarines were equipped with a deck gun, seven torpedoes (two tubes at the bow and one at the stern), as well as six mine chutes carrying a total of 18 mines. At the time of its loss the *UC-42* was manned by 26 or 27 crew members, who were commanded by *Oberleutnant zur See* Hans-Albrecht Müller.

During World War I such submarines were active along the Irish coastline laying mines, a dangerous task that sometimes resulted in U-boats being accidentally sunk by their own deadly delivery. In the case of *UC-42*, this appears to have happened on 10 September 1917, while it was attempting to lay mines across the mouth of Cork harbour in an effort to hinder shipping in the area. The U-boat's loss went unnoticed until 31 October, when British naval vessels minesweeping in the area detected a trail of oil floating on the sea surface just south of Roches Point. Following the detonation of a couple of depth charges, the seabed was inspected by divers on 2 November. They confirmed that there was indeed a German submarine below, which was identified as the wreck of *UC-42*. They found that the stern of the submarine had been destroyed when one of the mines it had been releasing detonated prematurely. The forward and conning tower hatches were open, possibly as a result of the crew trying to escape. Certain materials were recovered from the wreck, including the periscope, a telephone buoy and the vessel's log, with the last entry recorded on 10 September.

The sunken submarine remained a significant hazard to shipping in the area due to the mines and torpedoes contained within her hull, and in 1918 a number of attempts were made by divers to remove these armaments.

Below: The outline of the *UC-42* is clearly visible in the 3D multibeam imagery. The wreck lies on a sandy seabed with areas of rock outcrop to the SE of the wreck.

In July 1919 an attempt was made to destroy the wreck of the submarine by explosive charges, and to disperse the remains with wire sweeps. Since the 1970s numerous attempts have been made by divers to locate *UC-42*, but it was not until 2010 that the wreck was finally discovered during a survey for the Kinsale Gas Storage Project, carried out by the Marine Institute and Hydrographic Surveys Ltd. The wreck was identified by Moore Marine 2.25km northwest of the reported location of its sinking during the archaeological assessment of the sidescan sonar and multibeam data.

On the seafloor

The wreck of the *UC-42* measures 35m in length, 5m in width and 3.5m in maximum height. The vessel is lying on its port side and is orientated NW–SE on the seafloor, with its bow to the SE. At the time of its original discovery, in 1917, it was heavily depth charged and the results of that are still apparent on the wreck. While the inner pressure hull is essentially intact, almost all of the outer hull is gone bar the port saddle tank; however towards the keel aft of this area the concussive effect of the depth charges on the steel can be seen very clearly. What survives of the steel plating looks more like a sheet of wax that has been softened and draped over the frames beneath. The six mine chutes are clearly visible, three still with deteriorating mines within, and the external port torpedo tube can be found at the bow with the skeletal port forward hydroplane nearby. Aft of the mine chutes the gun mount is visible, but the conning tower is missing and can now be found aft near the stern on the starboard side. A little judicious cleaning of the marine growth on the starboard propeller has revealed the identity of the U-boat and other details stamped in the bronze. Adjacent to the propellers the stump of the stern torpedo tube protrudes through the pressure hull. There are a number of openings in the pressure hull aft of the mine chutes and the batteries that lined the sides of the forward section can be seen within.

Above: Torpedo tube on the *UC-42*. (Photo Timmy Carey)

Above: Propeller of the *UC-42* covered in sea anemones. (Photo Timmy Carey)

Printed Sources
Grant 2002, 71
Kieran & Hayden 2011
Kemp 1997, 34
Mallmann Showell 2006, 136
Möller & Brack 2004, 58

Nolan & Nolan 2009, 235
Stokes 2004, 169–70
Stokes 2011

Internet source
www.uboat.net

SS Etal Manor

GSI ref. code	214
NMS wreck no.	W04890
Location	14km S of Hook Head, Co. Wexford
Co-ordinates	52 0 12.46N, 006 53 57.52W
Depth of water	58m
Vessel type	Steam Collier
Vessel dimensions	82m (l), 12m (b), 5m (d)
Date of building	1916
Date of loss	19 September 1917

Circumstances of loss

The SS *Etal Manor* was a 1,875-ton steel steamship owned by John Fenwick & Son of London. The vessel was built in 1916 by J. Crown & Sons Ltd., of Sunderland, and propelled by 199 horsepower, triple-expansion engines capable of 9 knots. While en route from Barry in Wales to Cobh (then Queenstown), carrying a cargo of 2,550 tons of coal, the *Etal Manor* was torpedoed without warning and sunk by *UC-48*, under the command of *Oberleutnant zur*

See Kurt Ramien. Six lives were lost, including the master of the vessel. The *Etal Manor* was one of four vessels sunk by *UC-48* off the Wexford and Waterford coasts over a four-day period in September 1917.

On the seafloor

The wreck of the SS *Etal Manor* measures 93m in length, 19m in width and 1.9m in maximum height, with an average height of 1.4m. The vessel is orientated NNW–SSE on the seafloor and appears to be almost buried. A sediment scour has developed at the S end of the vessel.

Printed Sources
Hocking 1969, 229
Larn & Larn 2002
Roche 1993, 120, 132

Tennent 1990, 88
UKHO Wreck Data 1996

Internet Source
www.uboat.net

Below: A 3D, multibeam image of the SS *Etal Manor* lying on the seabed 14km S of Hook Head. The wreck is largely levelled, although the stern appears to be the highest part, standing almost 2m above the surrounding seabed.

SS W.M. Barkley

GSI ref. code	265
NMS wreck no.	W02101
Location	26km E of Howth Head, Co. Dublin
Co-ordinates	53 22 17.76N, 005 39 32.04W
Depth of water	49m
Vessel type	Cargo vessel
Vessel dimensions	54.5m (l), 8.25m (b), 3.78m (d)
Date of building	1898
Date of loss	12 October 1917

Above: High resolution multibeam image of the SS *W.M. Barkley,* which lies in a general sea depth of 56m. The bow *(on the right)* has separated from the main body of wreckage as a result of the damage caused by the original torpedo strike. A deep sediment scour has developed at the E end of the vessel, exposing its crippled bow.

Circumstances of loss

The SS *W.M. Barkley* was launched as a coaster in June 1898 by the Ailsa Shipbuilding Company in Troon, Scotland. Weighing 569 tons, it was propelled by an 80 horsepower, two-cylinder compression engine. The vessel was originally owned by W.M. Barkley & Son of Belfast and had operated as a collier before being acquired in 1911 by another firm in the same city, John Kelly & Sons. In December 1913 it became the first steamship to be owned by the producers of Guinness stout, Arthur Guinness & Sons Ltd of Dublin. When war broke out in 1914 the *W.M. Barkley* and other Guinness ships were commandeered by the British Admiralty and used to transport cargo, mainly to France. In 1917 the vessel was returned to the Dublin brewery as the Admiralty had decided that the steamship's heavy consumption of coal made her uneconomical for its uses.

Below: Painting of the SS *W.M. Barkley* under steam as exhibited in the Guinness Storehouse, Dublin. (Courtesy of Diageo Ireland)

On 12 October 1917, while en route from Dublin to Liverpool carrying a delivery of stout, the SS *W.M. Barkley* was torpedoed without warning by *UC-75*, under the command of *Oberleutnant zur See* Johannes Lohs. The cargo of barrels helped keep the vessel afloat long enough to enable some of the crew to launch a lifeboat and make good their escape from the sinking vessel. The steamship sank with the loss of four lives, including the ship's master, J. Simple. Casks of Guinness washed ashore along the coasts of Ireland and Wales in the days following the incident and no doubt the unsuspecting recipients of the sea's – and Guinness' – largesse were very grateful indeed. A model of the SS *W.M. Barkley* is on display in the Guinness Storehouse, Dublin.

On the seafloor

The wreck of the SS *W.M. Barkley* appears to be largely intact, measuring 67m long and 9m in maximum width. The vessel lies in a general sea depth of 56m and is orientated NE–SW. A sediment scour has developed at the NE end of the vessel, exposing its crippled bow. Diving on the *W.M. Barkley* can be challenging as the visibility on the wreck is usually quite poor. The counter stern is intact, although the deck plating has been corroded away and the midships' superstructure, with the hole for the funnel in the middle, is clearly discernible. The wooden decking has largely collapsed along the length of the wreck, exposing the ship's holds below. Forward the wreck is broken up in the vicinity of the torpedo strike and the bow is essentially separate from the main body of wreckage.

Printed Sources

Brady 2008, 47, 386

Larn & Larn 2002

Stokes 2004, 189–226

Tennent 1990, 112

U-58

GSI ref. code	290
NMS wreck no.	W10138
Location	20km S of Power Head, Co. Cork
Co-ordinates	51 36 20.316N, 008 09 53.52W
Depth of water	77m
Vessel type	U-boat
Vessel dimensions	67m (l), 6.32m (b), 3.79m (d)
Date of building	1916
Date of loss	17 November 1917

Circumstances of loss

U-58 is one of 15 German submarines that were destroyed in Irish waters during World War I. It is particularly interesting because it is the only U-boat definitely sunk by the U.S. Navy during the war. It was one of only 12 type U-57s ever constructed, being built in the A.G. Weser shipyard in Bremen in 1916. It was launched on 31 May that year and was commissioned into service on 9 August 1916. Type U-57 submarines were capable of speeds of 14.7 knots on the surface and 8.4 knots underwater. They had a surface weight of 786 tons, could reach a depth of *c.* 50m and carried a crew of 36 men. They were armed with 11 torpedoes and two deck guns – one 10.5cm and one 8.8cm gun.

On 10 November 1917, *U-58* departed Wilhelmshaven for its eighth, and what turned out to be its final, patrol. Four days later, in the English Channel, it sank the *Dolly Varden*, a 202-ton British sailing ship; there was no loss of life. The *U-58* proceeded to the Irish coast and on 15 November positioned itself at the approaches to Cork harbour to attack Allied vessels leaving port. Two days later it was spotted by USS *Fanning* and another destroyer,

Below: The US Navy Recruiting Bureau was quick to exploit the sinking of *U-58*. A range of postcards, adverts and posters was issued to encourage young men to sign up and play their part in defeating the German U-boat threat. (Ian Lawler Collection)

From a photograph taken on the U. S. S. Fanning

Press of U. S. Navy Recruiting Bureau New York

THE NAVY'S FIRST U-BOAT CAPTURE

We got them. Here they are, captured by the *Fanning* and the *Nicholson,* holding out their hands shouting "Kamerad". Forty-two minutes after the tip of the periscope of this U-boat had been sighted, the Germans were prisoners on board our ships. Some were picked up by our own men who jumped overboard.

Such is the speed of the Navy, always on the job.

LAD! IF YOU WANT ACTION, GET IN THE GAME AND ENLIST IN THE NAVY.

RECRUITING STATIONS EVERYWHERE

USS *Nicholson*, which attempted to sink the U-boat with a series of depth charges. Despite making an emergency descent, the depth charges destroyed the hydroplanes of the *U-58*, making it impossible to control the submarine underwater. The disabled U-boat was forced to surface and came under gunfire from the two destroyers. Given their untenable situation, *Kapitänleutnant* Gustav Amberger ordered his crew to assemble on deck to surrender and await rescue. Two crew members returned below to scuttle the submarine with explosive charges or by opening the seacocks, and as they re-emerged the submarine began to sink. Amberger and his crew jumped from the sinking vessel into the sea and were rescued by USS *Fanning*, except for two officers: one who drowned; and a second officer who died on board the *Fanning* and was later buried at sea. The captured crew were taken to Cobh, before being transferred to the custody of the Royal Navy and transported onwards to Britain. The *U-58* had been in service for 13 months, during which time it had sunk 21 ships, with the loss of 17 lives and 30,906 tons of shipping.

On the seafloor

The wreck of the *U-58* was discovered in 2010 during a survey of the Kinsale Gas Storage Project carried out by the Marine Institute and Hydrographic Surveys Ltd. The wreck was identified by Moore Marine 2.7km SE of the reported location of its sinking during an archaeological assessment of the sidescan sonar and multibeam data. The *U-58* was ground-truthed at the time using a Remotely Operated Vehicle (ROV). It measures 64.5m in length,

7.5m in width and 6m in height. The wreck appears to be sitting upright on the seabed and is orientated WNW–ESE. There are nets snagged on the wreck and there is a debris field surrounding the site.

Printed Sources
Grant 2002, 68
Kieran & Hayden 2011
Kemp 1997, 38
Mallmann Showell 2006, 145–6

Möller & Brack 2004, 29
Nolan & Nolan 2009, 254–5
Stokes 2004, 176, 239

Internet Source
www.uboat.net

Below: Multibeam image of the wreck sitting upright on the seabed. It is in poor condition in places and there is a large amount of wreck debris on the surrounding seabed. The outer hull plating at the bow and stern appears to be largely gone, exposing both sets of torpedo tubes.

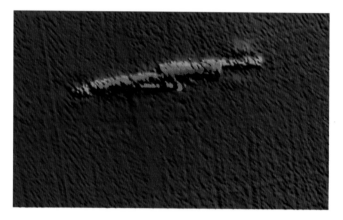

Opposite: The depth charges dropped by the USS *Fanning* – examples of which are seen here on its aft deck – damaged the hydroplanes of the *U-58*, forcing it to surface and surrender. This marked the first time a German U-boat was successfully attacked by a US naval vessel. (Ian Lawler Collection)

Below: A postcard of the USS *Fanning* in its dazzle camouflage, issued to celebrate the sinking of the *U-58*. (Ian Lawler Collection)

Hare

GSI ref. code	185
NMS wreck no.	W02024
Location	22km E of Howth Head, Co. Dublin
Co-ordinates	53 24 1.44N, 005 42 55.80W
Depth of water	65m
Vessel type	Merchant Steamship
Vessel dimensions	66m (l), 9m (b), 4m (d)
Date of building	1886
Date of loss	14 December 1917

Circumstances of loss

Although lost in tragic circumstances off the coast of Dublin during World War I, the *Hare* is in fact probably better known for the important role it played during the 1913 Lockout, an iconic moment in the history of the city of Dublin and the Irish trade union movement. The *Hare* became known as the 'First Ship' or the 'Food Ship' after it transported 340 tons of food and provisions to starving Dublin workers and their families, who had been on strike for nine months in pursuit of better pay, living and working conditions. The leaders of the Irish trade union movement, James Larkin and James Connolly, had appealed for assistance from abroad, and the trade unions in Manchester responded with great generosity by sending 60,000 'family boxes' full of essential foodstuffs, etc. Heartily welcomed by thousands of strikers, these much-needed supplies arrived in Dublin on the *Hare* on 28 September 1913.

The *Hare* was a 774-ton merchant steamship owned by George Lowen & Co., of Manchester. It was built in 1886 by Barclay Curle & Co., Whiteinch, Glasgow, and was powered by triple-expansion engines, enabling the vessel to achieve a speed of 9 knots. On its final voyage it was en route from Manchester to Dublin with 21 crewmen and carrying a 470-ton cargo, including foodstuffs. The *Hare* was torpedoed without warning by *U-62*, under the command of *Kapitänleutnant* Ernst Hashagen, and it was sunk within minutes. Six crewmen, including Captain Carmichael, managed to launch a lifeboat and were rescued by a passing steamer, while five more crew members were found clinging to an upturned lifeboat by a naval vessel that had arrived at the scene of the sinking to offer assistance. The remaining ten crew members (some sources say 12), who nearly all hailed from Dublin, were less fortunate and did not survive the disaster. The *U-62* was to strike again and sink two other vessels in the Irish Sea in December 1917, with the loss of 60 lives.

On the seafloor

The wreck of the *Hare* is orientated NE–SW on the seafloor and measures 45m long by 10m wide. It has a maximum height of 10.7m and appears to be broken in two. Deep sediment scouring has occurred around the vessel, indicative of the strong currents that occur in this area.

Printed Sources

Brady 2008, 377
Hocking 1989, 301
The Irish Times, 20 December 1917

Larn & Larn 2002
Tennent 1990, 157
UKHO Wreck data 1996

Below: Multibeam overview of the wreck of the SS *Hare* lying on the seabed. Deep sediment scouring has occurred around the vessel, indicating the strong currents that occur in this area.

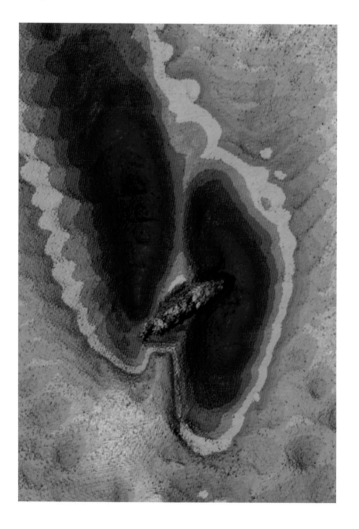

Maxton

GSI ref. code	14
NMS wreck no.	W07487
Location	68km NW of Malin Head, Co. Donegal
Co-ordinates	55 53 26.88N, 007 59 11.90W
Depth of water	166m
Vessel type	Cargo vessel
Vessel dimensions	114m (l), 15m (b)
Date of building	1912
Date of loss	28 December 1917

Circumstances of loss

The *Maxton* was a British steam cargo ship built by Irvine's Shipbuilding & Drydock Co. Ltd, West Hartlepool. The vessel weighed 3,840 tons and was powered by a triple-expansion engine. It was originally called the *Start Point* when completed in April 1912, and was operated by the Norfolk & North American S.S. Co. Ltd., West Hartlepool, until transferred to its mother company, Furness, Withy & Company, in 1915. It was subsequently renamed *Maxton*. The vessel was torpedoed by *U-19* and sunk 68km northwest of Malin Head while en route from Glasgow to Philadelphia with general cargo. There was one life lost. The *Maxton* was one of two vessels sunk by *U-19* (under the command of *Kapitänleutnant* Johannes Spiess) off the

Donegal coast on 28 December 1917, the other being the *Santa Amalia*, with the loss of 43 lives. Although both the *Santa Amalia* and the *Maxton* were recorded as sinking at the same location, the *Santa Amalia* is thought to be located 30km east of the *Maxton*'s final resting site.

On the seafloor

The wreck of the *Maxton* was discovered by the salvage company Risdon Beazley Marine Ltd in 1969 at a water depth of 166m, lying upright on the seabed with a slight list to its port side. Today, the wreck is orientated N–S on the seabed and what survives of it measures 40m in length, 13m in width and stands up to 7.8m above the seafloor. The resolution from the multibeam image is poor due to the significant water depth and the relatively small size of the vessel on the seabed.

Printed Sources
BVLS 1914–1918
PP 1919, Vol. XLII, 77
Tennent 1990, 94

Internet Sources
www.teesbuiltships.co.uk
www.theshipslist.com
www.uboat.net
www.wrecksite.eu

Below: This postcard reproduces a 1917 painting by German artist Willy Stöwer (1864–1931), which shows a U-boat crew looking on as an Allied troopship they torpedoed sinks stern-first beneath the waves. (Ian Lawler Collection)

U-89

GSI ref. code	276
NMS wreck no.	W07703
Location	38.5km NNW of Malin Head, Co. Donegal
Co-ordinates	55 42 19.39N, 007 34 47.69W
Depth of water	56m
Vessel type	U-boat
Vessel dimensions	65m (l), 6m (b), 4m (d)
Date of building	1916
Date of loss	13 February 1918

Circumstances of loss

Over 180 German U-boats were destroyed or sunk during combat in World War I and *U-89* is one of approximately 15 such submarines sunk off the coast of Ireland during this period. The vessel was one of 40 U-81 class German submarines commissioned during the war. It weighed 808 tons, measured 65m long and could carry a crew of 36 men. It was capable of 16.8 knots, had 2,400 horsepower engines and a range of 11,380 miles travelling on the surface. The U-81 class German submarine could reach a maximum depth of 50m.

The *U-89* was built by Kaiserliche Werft of Danzig and was commissioned into service on 21 June 1917. It carried out three patrols during its service with the III Flotilla and during the period 6 September 1917–12 February 1918 it successfully sunk four ships and damaged one other. In early 1918 *U-89* was patrolling the North Channel between Malin Head and the Scottish mainland, under the command of *Kapitänleutnant* Wilhelm Bauck. On 10 February it observed a convoy proceeding out of the North

Channel under escort, but it was too far away and moving too fast for the *U-89* to engage it. Two days later *U-89* was still patrolling the area when it surfaced, unaware that it was in the direct course of the HMS *Roxburgh*, one of the vessels that had been escorting the convoy seen two days earlier. Lieutenant Commander Smithwick of the *Roxburgh*, seeing the submarine surfacing, immediately directed the cruiser towards the helpless *U-89*, ramming it, resulting in its immediate loss. The submarine appeared to explode and sank immediately, with the loss of all 43 crew aboard. When the *Roxburgh* returned to port, part of the submarine was still impaled on the bow of the cruiser.

On the seafloor

The wreck of the *U-89* measures 53m in length, 7m in width and 6m in height. It is orientated E–W on the seafloor and appears to be lying on its side, with the conning tower clearly visible amidships. Its bow lies to the east. This wreck is an eye-opener for those more used to diving WWII U-boats. The first thing that strikes the diver is the sheer size of the vessel, which is as big as the WWII Type VII submarine. As with many submarine wrecks, the internal pressure hull is essentially intact and much of the outer hull has corroded away, however the huge saddle ballast tanks are still clearly visible amidships. Aft the stern two torpedo tubes can be seen and further forward, on the port side, the damage inflicted by the bow of HMS *Roxburgh* has exposed the two gigantic diesel engines. The aft 88mm gun sits on the deck behind the conning tower; the forward 105mm gun is also present. At the bow the skeletal remains of the hydroplanes can be seen either side of the hull. If the diver peers into the hatch of the torpedo room, a fully intact torpedo, with contra-rotating

Below: Crew members on board *U-89*. (Courtesy of the Deutsches U-boot Museum)

propellers, can be seen on the floor. The bow outside the pressure hull has corroded away and the four unsupported torpedo tubes have now fallen onto the seabed below. Their complete collapse has been arrested by the presence of torpedoes in a number of the tubes, the tails of which remain jammed in the pressure hull. This is definitely not a sight for the faint-hearted given that these warheads are still 'live'!

Above: Artist's impression of the ramming of the *U-89* by the HMS *Roxburgh*, which was on naval escort duties off the Donegal coast. The *U-89* unwittingly surfaced in the path of the HMS *Roxburgh*, which duly rammed it, nearly splitting the submarine in two with the loss of all 43 submariners. (Ian Lawler Collection)

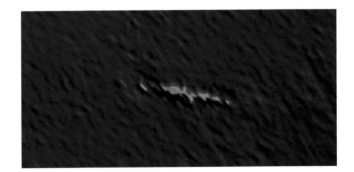

Above: Multibeam view of the 53m long wreck of the *U-89*, which is listing to the starboard side.

Printed Sources

Chatterton 1943, 121–2
Grant 2002, 111
Kemp 1997, 124
Larn & Larn 2002
Möller & Brack 2004, 33
Rossler 1981, 54–5
Tierney 2005, 14–15

Internet Sources

www.uboat.net

Amazon

GSI ref. code	33
NMS wreck no.	W07115
Location	68km N of Bloody Foreland, Co. Donegal
Co-ordinates	55 46 15.13N, 008 11 21.98W
Depth of water	113m
Vessel type	Passenger Liner
Vessel dimensions	161.5m (l), 18m (b), 9m (d)
Date of building	1906
Date of loss	15 March 1918

Above: A 3D, multibeam view of the wreck from the SW.

Opposite, top: 'Gentlemen' enjoying the after-dinner comforts of the first-class smoking room, which was restricted exclusively for male use only. (Ian Lawler Collection)

Opposite, bottom: The RMS Amazon was the one of five 'A Class' passenger liners built for the Royal Mail Line's transatlantic service between England, Brazil and Argentina. The lavishly decorated social hall was one of the many onboard amenities that could be enjoyed by both male and female first-class passengers. (Ian Lawler Collection)

Circumstances of loss

The *Amazon* was a 10,037-ton, twin-screw passenger liner built by Harland & Wolff Ltd. in Belfast in 1906. This single-funnelled steamship was owned by the Royal Mail Steam Packet Company, London, and could carry up to 870 passengers on three decks. It had a maximum speed of 15 knots, which made it suitable for commission on the transatlantic mail and passenger service between England, Brazil and Argentina. It was on one such voyage that the *Amazon* was attacked and sunk by a German U-boat. The *Amazon*, under the command of Captain H.D. Doughty, was not long into its voyage from Liverpool to Buenos Aires when *U-110*, under the command of *Korvettenkapitän* Karl Kroll, torpedoed the liner without warning 30 miles northwest of Malin Head. The *Amazon* quickly began to sink, but miraculously the crew and all 870 passengers were rescued within 15 minutes by two nearby Royal Naval destroyers, the HMS *Michael* and *Moresby*, which came to the stricken vessel's assistance. Following the rescue, the same destroyers released depth charges, forcing *U-110* to surface. The 43 submariners abandoned the fatally damaged U-boat, which sank soon afterwards at 55 49N, 08 06W; only four of the crew managed to survive exposure to the cold Atlantic waters. Prior to this incident *U-110* had sunk nine other ships, including the *Castle Eden*, which had been lost off the Donegal coastline 11 days earlier.

On the seafloor

The wreck of the *Amazon* measures 168m in length, 29m in width and is orientated NNW–SSE on the seafloor. As with all wrecks in the deep waters off Donegal, the visibility generally becomes gin-clear below 40m, whereas the warmer upper layers often contain a planktonic soup. Visibility on the wreck itself varies between 20 and 40m and this reveals a rare sight in diving: a completely upright wreck. She is so level with the seabed that some of the side hull plating has fallen inwards and some has fallen outwards. On descent and at about 80m, the diver can clearly see the wreck rise up 7m or more above the sandy seabed, like a spectral silhouette. The bow is cocked upwards, as if she was driven into the seabed; the split between the port and starboard sections of the upper bow area lends weight to this theory. The scour around the north-pointing bow is impressive, too. The bridge is difficult to discern from the first-class area as the *Amazon* was an 'old-fashioned' liner, having a separate bridge and passenger area above deck level. The stern lies to the south and, by contrast, rises only a few metres above seabed level.

Printed Sources
Kemp 1997, 45
Larn & Larn 2002
Williams 1997, 70

Internet Source
www.uboat.net

Following pages: Postcard of the 10,037-ton Royal Mail Steam Packet Company passenger liner *Amazon* under steam. (Ian Lawler Collection)

Myrtle Branch

GSI ref. code	95
NMS wreck no.	W07506
Location	21km N of Inishtrahull, Co. Donegal
Co-ordinates	55 37 18.19N, 007 13 27.05W
Depth of water	58m
Vessel type	Cargo vessel
Vessel dimensions	116m (l), 14m (b), 8m (d)
Date of building	1899
Date of loss	11 April 1918

Above: German propaganda postcard depicting U-boats at work enforcing a blockade of England.

Below: Multibeam image of the 112m-long wreck on the seabed that was broken up by salvage operations. The salvage works were carried out in 1954 by Risdon Beazley Marine Ltd., which recovered much of the cargo of metal ores. The boilers are still relatively intact (*red spikes*), standing 7.3m proud of the seabed amidships.

Circumstances of loss

The *Myrtle Branch*, formerly known as the *Isel Holme*, was a 3,741-ton steel steamship owned by the Nautilus Steam Ship Co. Ltd. (F.W. Ritson of Sunderland). The vessel was built in 1899 by J.L. Thompson and Sons, Sunderland, and was propelled by a 336 horsepower, three-cylinder, triple-expansion engine. On 11 April 1918, while en route from South America to Liverpool, the *Myrtle Branch* was torpedoed without warning by *UB-73*, under the command of *Oberleutnant zur See* Karl Neureuther. The steamship sank with the loss of 15 crew, including the master of the vessel, Captain J. McClalland. The vessel was carrying 1,028 tons of metal ores. In 1954 the salvage company Risdon Beazley Marine Ltd. recovered most of this cargo, which included tin ore, antimony ore, lead ore, bismuth ore, copper precipitate, silver sulphide, wolfram ore and silver ore.

On the seafloor

The wreck of the *Myrtle Branch* measures 112m in length and 19m in width, with an average height of 1.6m. The vessel is orientated NE–SW on the seafloor, with its boilers standing 7.3m proud of the seabed. There is sediment scouring at the NE end of the vessel. Little of the graceful clipper bow and stern protrude above the seafloor and little else recognisable remains after the salvage operations to recover her cargo of metal ores. Amongst the scattered iron plates, only the boilers amidships and the rudder quadrant and sternpost are identifiable as parts of a ship.

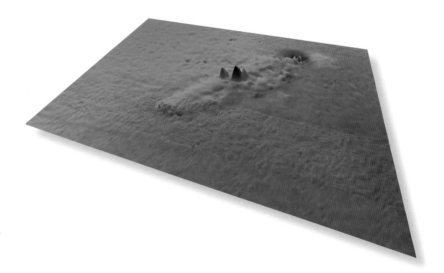

Printed Sources
Hocking 1969, 491
Larn & Larn 2002
PP 1919, Vol. LXII, 86
Tennent 1990, 195–6
UKHO Wreck Data 1996

Internet Source
www.uboat.net

SS Fern

GSI ref. code	264
NMS wreck no.	W02012
Location	20km E of Ireland's Eye, off the coast of Co. Dublin
Co-ordinates	53 25 51.24N, 005 46 56.28W
Depth of water	76m
Vessel type	Steamship
Vessel dimensions	54.9m (l), 8.8m (b), 3.68m (d)
Date of building	1900
Date of loss	22 April 1918

Circumstances of loss

The SS *Fern* was a 444-ton steamship built in 1900 by the Ailsa Shipbuilding Company for the Scottish-based Glasgow, Dublin & Londonderry Steam Packet Company (the Laird Line). The steamship was propelled by 120 horsepower, triple-expansion engines and was capable of achieving 8.5 knots. The *Fern* was brought into direct ownership of the Laird Line Ltd, Glasgow, in 1908. On 22 April 1918, while en route from Dublin to Heysham with a general cargo, the vessel was torpedoed and sunk without warning by *U-104*, under the command of *Kapitänleutnant* Kurt Bernis. All 13 crew on board the *Fern*, including Captain D. MacArthur, were killed in the attack. The *Fern* was one of eight ships sunk by *U-104* during the war. The submarine's roll call of destruction was ended just three days after the loss of the *Fern*, when it too was lost after being depth-charged and sunk by the HMS *Jessamine* approximately 21km south of Carnsore Point, Co. Wexford. Forty-one of the crew on board the U-boat, including *Kapitänleutnant* Kurt Bernis, were killed, with only one crew member surviving the attack.

On the seafloor

The wreck of the SS *Fern* lies in a general sea depth of 79m and is largely intact on the seabed. It is orientated E–W and measures 50.1m in length, 7.1m in width and 10.67m in maximum height. The wreck is located at the southeastern end of the Lambay Deep, which is one of the deepest parts of the Irish Sea, reaching depths of more than 130m.

Printed Sources
BVLS 1919, 87
Brady 2008, 376
Hocking 1969, 240
Larn & Larn 2002

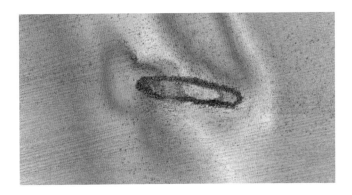

Above: The wreck of the *Fern* stands out against the sandy and muddy seabed in the multibeam data. Two large areas of scouring are visible around the E end and N side of the wreck, indicating the strong currents and tidal movements in the area.

Above: Laird Line poster advertising tours around Ireland in 1908. (TD 644/37, Glasgow Life Archives)

SS Polwell

GSI ref. code	255
NMS wreck no.	W02067
Location	8km NE of Lambay Island, off the coast of Co. Dublin
Co-ordinates	53 33 12N, 005 55 56.4W
Depth of water	30m
Vessel type	British Steam Collier
Vessel dimensions	86.56m (l), 11.6m (b), 5.5m (d)
Date of building	1888
Date of loss	5 June 1918

Circumstances of loss

The SS *Polwell* was originally named the *Northumbria* when it was built in 1888, in Sunderland, by J.L. Thompson & Son. It weighed 2,013 in gross tonnage and was powered by a 201 horsepower, three-cylinder, triple-expansion engine. The vessel changed hands a number of times in its lifetime. In 1910 it was sold to a German company in Szczecin, Poland, and renamed the *Deutscher Kaiser*. In 1914 it was sold and re-registered as the *Syra*, and was then based in Hamburg. Shortly after this, while en route from Antwerp to the Levant, it was captured off Gibraltar and requisitioned by the British Admiralty. Under the control of the Shipping Controller, the *Syra* was renamed the SS *Polwell* and operated as an armed steam collier from 1917 to 1918, managed by the Clyde Shipping Co. Ltd., Glasgow.

On 4 June 1918 the *Polwell* left Troon, Scotland, for France, with a cargo of coal to supply the Allied war effort. As the *Polwell* approached the Irish coast the following morning, a warning shot was fired across its bows by *U-96*, commanded by *Kapitänleutnant* Heinrich Jess. The 30 crew on board abandoned the collier and

Below: The SS *Polwell* was renamed several times following its launch as the *Northumbria* in 1888 in Sunderland. The collier is pictured here some time between 1910 and 1914, when it was known as the *Deutscher Kaiser*. (Ian Lawler Collection)

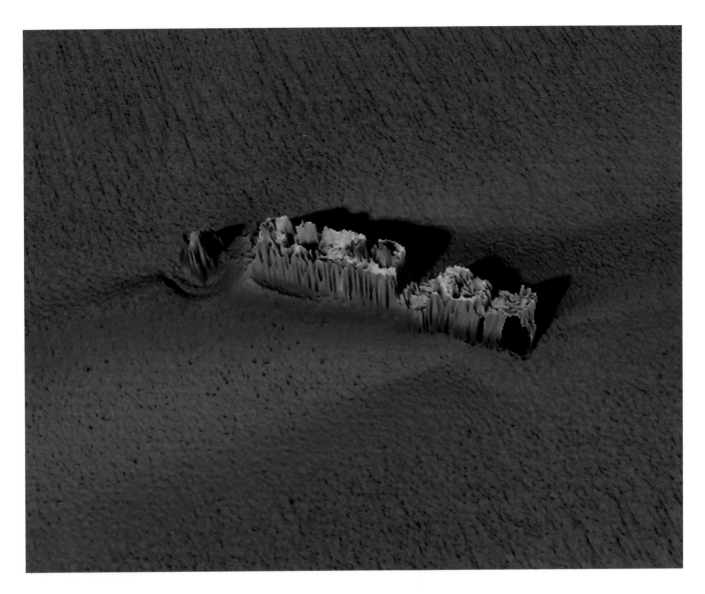

took to the two lifeboats. The *U-96* fired a single torpedo at the *Polwell*, hitting it amidships and causing it to sink immediately, 8km northeast of Lambay Island, off the north Dublin coast. All of the *Polwell*'s 30 crew managed to land safely at Rockabill lighthouse one hour later. The SS *Polwell* was one of 31 ships sunk by *U-96* between 1917 and 1918.

On the seafloor

The wreck of the SS *Polwell* measures 92m in length, 11.4m in width and 8.34m in maximum height. It is orientated NE–SW on the seafloor, with its bow to the NE. The wreck is remarkably intact, particularly amidships where the remains of the bridge and deckhouse over the engine room are visible. Forward past the first hold a curtain of trawl nets suspended from floats can be quite a sight in good visibility, and a positive hazard in poor visibility. This marks where the wreck has collapsed,

Above: A 3D, multibeam image of the 92m-long wreck that lies upright on the seabed, 8km NE of Lambay Island. It shows the remains of the bridge and deckhouse over the engine room amidships, and areas of collapse around the forward and aft holds. Also visible are the bow, *c.* 10m away, and the counter stern, standing almost upright.

in the vicinity of the forward hold. The bow is now 10m or so from the main body of the wreck and it too is draped in a large tangle of trawl net. There is further collapse evident in the vicinity of the aft hold, however the counter stern still stands upright. Part of the cargo of coal is reported to be still present on the wreck.

Printed Sources
Brady 2008, 382
BVLS 1914–1918
King 1977
Larn & Larn 2002

Justicia

GSI ref. code	58
NMS wreck no.	W07410
Location	38km NW of Malin Head, Co. Donegal
Co-ordinates	55 39 46.98N, 007 43 13.12W
Depth of water	67m
Vessel type	Passenger Liner
Vessel dimensions	226m (l), 26m (b), 13m (d)
Date of building	1914
Date of loss	20 July 1918

Circumstances of loss

This 32,234-ton steel steamship was originally built by Harland & Wolff for the Holland-Amerika Line as the *Statendam*, a liner capable of carrying 3,430 passengers. It was powered by triple-expansion engines, allowing for speeds up to 18 knots. The *Statendam* was launched on 9 July 1914 and was due to serve on transatlantic passenger

Above: A postcard depicting how the 32,234-ton *Justicia* may have looked had she been completed as the SS *Statendam*, as originally planned, for the Holland-Amerika Line. Due to the outbreak of war, the liner was requisitioned by the British Government and converted to a troopship in 1917. (Ian Lawler Collection)

Opposite: Divers investigate the still largely intact bow of the *Justicia*, which lies in 67m of water. (Photo Barry McGill)

service routes, but the British Government requisitioned the vessel and changed its name to *Justicia*, earmarking it for service as a troopship in 1917.

Under the management of the White Star Line, the *Justicia* entered service on 7 April 1917 and made several successful transatlantic trips, carrying American troops for service in Europe. The *Justicia* had a close call when it survived a U-boat attack in January 1918, when it had 600–700 crew on board, but no passengers. Later that year, on 19 July, the liner was en route from Liverpool to New York in convoy when it was attacked by *UB-64*, under the command of *Kapitänleutnant* Otto von Schrader. At 2.30pm a torpedo struck the engine room, and at 4.30pm two more torpedoes were fired: one missed its target; the other was diverted by gunfire. At 8.00pm a fourth torpedo was discharged, but gunfire again proved successful in diverting the aim. Naval escorts dropped depth charges that damaged the *UB-64*'s fuel tanks, forcing the U-boat to retreat from further attack. The next morning *UB-124*, on its first patrol, sighted the *Justicia* under tow, accompanied by a dozen escort destroyers. At 9.15am *UB-124* launched two torpedoes at the damaged vessel. Eventually, the *Justicia* sank, stern first, at 12.40pm, with the loss of 16 lives; the rest of the crew were rescued by nearby ships. The naval destroyers HMS *Marne*, *Millbrook* and *Pigeon* subsequently succeeded in sinking *UB-124*.

On the seafloor

The wreck of the *Justicia* measures 224m in length, 50m in width and 8m in maximum height, with an average height of 3.1m. The vessel is orientated N–S on the seafloor and shows some sediment scouring on the east side. Today, even 70m down, the ravages of the relentless Atlantic swell and corrosion have left this gigantic ship in a very broken state. She is still an impressive sight, however, and her majestic bow, still largely intact, is probably one of the most remarkable sights a diver can encounter in Irish waters. The starboard anchor, still in its hawse, dwarfs any visiting diver and epitomises the scale of this great ship. Gigantic capstans and windlasses dot the fo'c'sle, and aft past the giant forehold the bridge superstructure has collapsed down and to port, to rest with deck level on the seabed. Giant rectangular windows, each the size of a door, gaze sternly out over the foredeck. Behind that again lies the field of 12 giant Scotch boilers, each the size of a modern semi-detached house, followed by the two enormous eight-cylinder, triple-expansion steam engines. Just aft is the steam turbine, which was run by the exhaust steam from the two engines and drove the centre propeller shaft and which is often overlooked amongst the giant structures. This three-screw arrangement was pioneered by Harland & Wolff on the *Laurentic*, the wreck of which lies nearby, and also on the *Titanic* and her sister ships. The stern is fairly broken up now, but the stern gun and rudder quadrant are still visible.

Printed Sources

Bishop 2002, 51–6

Bishop 2004, 27–34

Bishop & Louden-Brown 2001, 8–14

Grant 1964, 113–14

Hocking 1989, 366

Williams 1997, 80–81

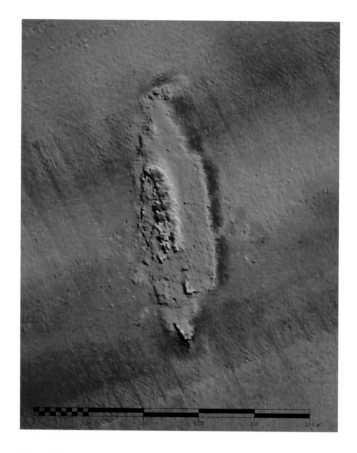

Above: The *Justicia* is clearly discernible against the stony seabed in the multibeam imagery. The 12 giant Scotch boilers, standing over 8m above the seabed, run in pairs along the length of the wreck, followed by the two enormous eight-cylinder, triple-expansion steam engines. A slight scour has developed at its S end (*lower section*), exposing the largely intact bow.

Opposite top: Postcard of the *UB-64* returning from its last patrol. The *UB-64*, along with the *UB-124*, was responsible for sinking the *Justicia*. The *UB-64* undertook eight war patrols between August 1917 and November 1918, sinking 29 ships and damaging four more. The *UB-64* surrendered on 21 November 1918 and was broken up at Fareham in 1921. (Ian Lawler Collection)

Opposite bottom: The *Justicia* painted in wartime dazzle camouflage. This technique of camouflaging a ship was employed on ships during WWI to make it difficult for enemy U-boats to determine the vessel's identity, type, heading and speed rather than trying to totally camouflage or conceal the ship. (Ian Lawler Collection)

Following pages: Gigantic capstans, bollards and windlasses still dominate the disintegrating deck area of the fo'c'sle. (Photo Barry McGill)

Rükkehr U-B. 64 von der letzten Fahrt.

Flavia

GSI ref. code	119
NMS wreck no.	W07330
Location	43km W of Tory Island, off the coast of Co. Donegal
Co-ordinates	55 16 45.88N, 008 54 52.24W
Depth of water	101m
Vessel type	Passenger Liner
Vessel dimensions	143m (l), 17m (b), 10m (d)
Date of building	1901
Date of loss	24 August 1918

Circumstances of loss

The *Flavia* was a 9,291-ton, twin-screw steam liner which at the time of its sinking was owned by the Cunard Steam Shipping Co Ltd., of Liverpool. It was built in 1901 by Palmer's Shipbuilding & Iron Co., in Jarrow-on-Tyne, and had several owners since its launch as the *British Empire* for the British Shipowners Company in August 1901. It had four masts, a single funnel and a maximum speed of 13 knots. Initially operated as a cargo ship between Antwerp and New York, it was refitted as a passenger liner in 1906 when it was purchased by Navigazione Generale Italiana and renamed the *Campania*. It operated on the Genoa–New York service between 1907 and 1909, and then the Hamburg–New York service, until purchased in 1910 by the Canadian Northern Steamship Co. The newly renamed *Campanello* was then chartered to the Uranium Steamship Co., operating on the Rotterdam–Halifax–New York service until 1914, and then on the Avonmouth–Quebec–Montreal service until 1916. It was at this stage that Cunard bought the Canadian Northern Steamship Co. and the Uranium Steamship Co. and had the liner renamed *Flavia*.

In August 1918 the *Flavia* departed Montreal for Avonmouth in a convoy of eight ships, with a general cargo and 750 horses. As the liner was

Below: The *Campania* was subsequently renamed the *Campanello* in 1910 when chartered to the Uranium Steamship Co., before being purchased again six years later and renamed the *Flavia* by the Cunard Steam Shipping Co. Ltd. (Ian Lawler Collection)

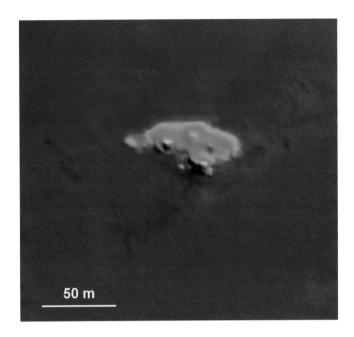

50 m

Above: The *Flavia* does not show up well in the multibeam data because the wreck is in poor condition, with most of the upper decks completely disintegrated.

Above: The German submarine *U-107* docked in the English port town of Weymouth, Norfolk, some time after the declaration of the armistice in November 1918. This submarine had torpedoed and sunk the *Flavia* the previous August, along with six other ships during the course of the war. (Courtesy of the National Maritime Museum, Greenwich)

nearing the northwest coast of Ireland it was attacked without warning by *U-107*, under the command of *Kapitänleutnant* Kurt Siewert. A torpedo hit number one forward hold, with a second torpedo striking the heavily listing ship and preventing the starboard lifeboats from being launched. The stricken *Flavia* sank soon afterwards and the survivors were rescued by the escorting destroyers and landed at Ardrossan, Scotland. One life was lost in the incident.

On the seafloor

The wreck of the *Flavia* measures 148m in length, 32m in width and 7m in maximum height, with an average height of 3.2m. The vessel is orientated NE–SW on the seafloor, with its bow to the southwest. It lists about 20 degrees to port and most of the upper decks are completely gone, leaving the boilers and machinery standing proud and completely exposed. Only a metre or two of the hull can be seen sticking out of the sand on the port side, whereas the starboard hull is 4–5m high in parts. The bow area is sinking into the sand, surviving simply as a lattice of steelwork with large winches, chain and some unusual 'inverted bell-shaped' fairleads (a device to guide a rope) being the only recognisable features. Her stern stands more proud than the bow and one propeller is visible, with two of the blades sticking out of the sand.

Above: The *Flavia* had several owners since its launch as the *British Empire* in 1901. This postcard shows the steamer as the Navigazione Generale Italiana-owned *Campania* (1906–10). (Ian Lawler Collection)

Printed Sources
Bonsor 1979, Vol. iii, 1117
Larn and Larn 2002
Smith 1947
Tennent 1990, 61–2

HMS Guide Me II

GSI ref. code	138
NMS wreck no.	W01482
Location	1.5km ESE of the Muglins, Dublin Bay
Co-ordinates	053 16 19.52N, 006 03 15.88W
Depth of water	33m
Vessel type	Anti-Submarine Drifter
Vessel dimensions	26m (l), 5.6m (b), 2.8m (d)
Date of building	1907
Date of loss	29 August 1918

Above: Side-scan sonar image of the 28m-long wreck lying upright on the seabed in Dublin Bay.

Circumstances of loss

Guide Me II grossed 100 tons and was built in 1907 by Hall, Russell & Co. Ltd., of Aberdeen. It initially operated as a net barrier tender in Peterhead and was owned by J. Mitchell & John Cow. In March 1915 it was hired by the Admiralty and converted into a British anti-submarine drifter (Admiralty drifter no. 2567), with one 6-pounder gun. It sank following an accidental collision with the SS *Glengarriff* of Cork, with the loss of one life. The wreck was discovered in 1990 and the gun was lifted and presented to the Maritime Museum in Dún Laoghaire.

On the seafloor

The wreck is orientated WNW–ESE on the seafloor and measures 28.5m in length and 5.5m in width, with a maximum height of 3m above the seabed. It lies with a slight list to the port side in a general sea depth of 32–35m. It is a popular dive site in Dublin Bay as it is still relatively intact. The vessel sits upright, slightly scoured into the seabed, with the hull completely intact bar the gash that sank her, which is cut into her starboard quarter. Aft much of the wheelhouse is still recognisable and lying beside the hull on the seabed to port is the funnel, usually inhabited by a large conger eel. Forward along the deck is the large, open fish hold and just aft of the bow a windlass and the base of the gun mount.

Printed Sources

Brady 2008, 285

Hepper 2006, 140

Larn & Larn 2002

UKHO Wreck Data 1996

Above: Close-up view of the *Guide Me II*.

RMS Leinster

GSI ref. code	153
NMS wreck no.	W02039
Location	19km ESE of Howth Head, Co. Dublin
Co-ordinates	53 18 51.48N, 005 47 34.22W
Depth of water	28m
Vessel type	Passenger Steamer
Vessel dimensions	110m (l), 13m (b), 8m (d)
Date of building	1896
Date of loss	10 October 1918

Circumstances of loss

The RMS *Leinster* was a 2,646-ton, twin-screw, steel steamer built in Birkenhead, Liverpool, in 1896 by Lairds. It was owned by the City of Dublin Steam Packet Company and worked the mail route between Ireland and Britain. The *Leinster* was the unfortunate victim of one of the worst maritime tragedies ever to take place in Irish waters. On 10 October 1918, 5 miles east of the Kish Light Vessel, *UB-123* torpedoed and sunk the *Leinster*, with the loss of 501 lives. The vessel had sailed since 1896 on the cross-channel mail delivery and passenger service, and could journey between Kingstown (Dún Laoghaire) and Holyhead in 2.5 hours. It had several close encounters with German U-boats throughout the war, but it was only with weeks to go before the November armistice that the vessel's luck finally ran out.

The *Leinster* left Carlisle Pier on 10 October, making for Holyhead with a general cargo, 250 sacks of mail and 771 passengers and crew. Over 400 of the passengers were soldiers. The captain was William Birch, an experienced seaman. Once outside the shelter of Dublin Bay, the vessel encountered SW force 5–6 winds and uncomfortable seas. Without warning, it was torpedoed by *UB-123*. The *Leinster* listed to the port and sank, bow first, within 15 minutes. A number of lifeboats capsized, drowning their occupants, but some passengers and crew successfully managed to launch lifeboats and were saved by the destroyers HMS *Mallard* and *Lively*, and the Motor Launch 154. Tragically, 501 of the 771 on board lost their lives. The anchor was raised from the seabed in 1996 and is now displayed on Dún Laoghaire promenade as a memorial to the victims of this tragic event.

On the seafloor

The wreck of the *Leinster* lies well buried in sand at a general depth of 25–28m and is orientated N–S. The bow is separated from the main vessel and the stern section is

Above: Diver investigates the main deck of the RMS *Leinster.* (Photo Brian Murray)

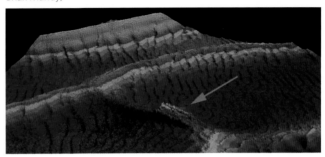

Above: A 3D, multibeam image of the N–S lying wreck on the seabed between two large sand waves. Parts of the wreck are buried due to high levels of sand movement here, but most of it sits 2–3m proud of the seafloor, making it possible to get a sense of the outline of the ship.

badly damaged, with the wreck site measuring 112m in length, 15.5m in width and 3.5m in maximum height, with an average height of 2.4m. A sediment scour has developed on its east side and the main body of the ship has settled deep into the sand. While the bow has been separated from the rest of the ship by the torpedo damage, about 53m of the wreck still remains relatively intact. Despite this, most of the wreck sits 2–3m proud of the seafloor and it is still possible to get a sense of a ship from the main section, while the holes where the two funnels once stood can be found amidships. The stern is now badly broken up and the rudder and steering quadrant sits 5m clear of the main body of the wreck. Due to its moderate depth and the usually reasonable visibility at the site, the *Leinster* remains one of the most popular wreck dives in Dublin Bay.

Printed Sources

Bourke 1994, 32
Brady 2008, 379, 401–4
De Courcy Ireland 1983, 139
Larn & Larn 2002

Lecane 2005, 13
Stokes 1998
Tennent 1990, 45
UKHO Wreck Data 1996

Following pages: The RMS *Leinster* in dazzle camouflage, painted by William Minshall Birchall (1884–1941). (Courtesy of the British Mercantile Marine Memorial Collection)

"Leinster" - Torpedoed off Kish Lightship 10.10.18
W.M.Birchall.

5 Ireland and World War II

James Lyttleton, Roy Stokes and Karl Brady

Ireland and the War at Sea, 1939–45

When the war broke out in September 1939 the Irish government, under Taoiseach Éamon de Valera, opted to maintain a policy of neutrality as the best means of protecting the country's population and economy. Britain was concerned, however, about the security of shipping in the western approaches, as the German Navy (*Kriegsmarine*) once again deployed a significant submarine presence in the Atlantic approaches to the north and south of Ireland. Ireland's neutrality was problematic in that the country didn't have the resources to make a major military contribution. Nonetheless, many Irish people joined the war effort in Britain and America, and in many ways Ireland was 'positively neutral' on the side of the Allies.

Ireland's neutral stance did not protect its waters from belligerent action and just as in World War I, the waters around Ireland became a deadly theatre of war, where hundreds of Allied vessels and German U-boats were lost. The *Kriegsmarine* sought to attack merchant shipping in an effort to cut off Britain's vital supply of food, oil, weapons and raw materials. Within hours of the declaration of hostilities, the passenger liner *Athenia*, sailing from Glasgow to Montreal, was attacked by *U-30* some 250 miles west of Inishtrahull Island, Co. Donegal (*see* p.124). Carrying 1,103 passengers and 315 crew, the liner was torpedoed after being mistaken for an armed merchant cruiser. Despite a speedy rescue response by a number of vessels in the area, 123 people lost their lives. This incident caused a huge outcry, with the British accusing Berlin of launching an unrestricted submarine campaign in Atlantic waters. The embarrassed German authorities – who had specifically forbidden such attacks at this stage of the war – alleged that the liner had been sunk by a British mine. When *U-30* returned to base, its log books were altered to cover up German culpability for the incident – the only known instance of a U-boat log book being doctored in such a manner during the entire course of the war.

When Germany overran France in 1940 and threatened an invasion of England, possibly via a co-ordinated invasion of Ireland, British anxiety grew stronger regarding the security of its western approaches. The fall of France allowed Admiral Karl Donitz, commander of the *Kriegsmarine*, to establish U-boat bases on the west coast of France, providing easier and faster access for German U-boats to British and Irish waters. The belief in a British pre-eminence on the seas could not be taken for granted either, as there was the threat that the German High Seas fleet could break out of the North Sea. The military situation was made more difficult given that Britain no longer had access to strategic ports on Ireland's southern and western coastline, having surrendered the Treaty ports of Cobh, Berehaven and Lough Swilly to de Valera's administration earlier in 1938. To preserve Ireland's non-belligerent status, and to retain possession of the sea ports and airbases that straddled the approaches to the Atlantic, a number of measures were agreed between the Irish and British governments, which gave Britain and its allies the security it sought while allowing Ireland to maintain its neutrality. These measures included permission for Allied patrols to fly into Irish airspace, and military liaison between the British and Irish armies.

The Marine and Coastwatching Service was established in 1939 to maintain a lookout around the Irish coast. A total of 83 lookout posts were constructed, which meant the entire coastline was under surveillance by the Irish authorities. Another important development came in 1941 with the formation of Irish Shipping Ltd. by the Irish Government, established to help secure necessary wartime supplies and food. This was the nucleus of the Irish merchant fleet, which would play an important role in the development of the Irish economy until 1984.

After Germany occupied France, the entrance to the Irish Channel was mined and the southern approaches were largely abandoned by the larger convoys in favour of the approaches to the north of Ireland. From July to

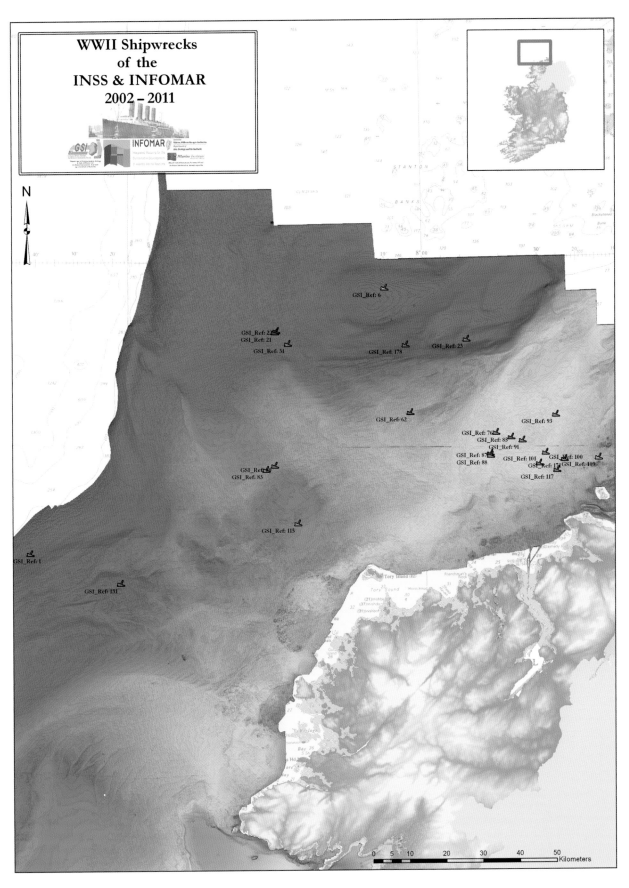

WWII Shipwrecks
of the
INSS & INFOMAR
2002 – 2011

N

GSI_Ref: 6

GSI_Ref: 2
GSI_Ref: 21
GSI_Ref: 31   GSI_Ref: 178   GSI_Ref: 23

GSI_Ref: 62   GSI_Ref: 93

GSI_Ref: 76
GSI_Ref: 85
GSI_Ref: 91
GSI_Ref: 87   GSI_Ref: 101   GSI_Ref: 100
GSI_Ref: 88   GSI_Ref: 171 GSI_Ref: 109
GSI_Ref: 117

GSI_Ref:
GSI_Ref: 83

GSI_Ref: 115

GSI_Ref: 1

GSI_Ref: 131

Legend

VESSEL TYPE

ARMED AUXILIARY CRUISER   CARGO VESSEL   MERCHANT SHIP   PASSENGER LINER   SUBMARINE (DEADLIGHT)   TRAWLER

ANTI AIRCRAFT CRUISER   ARMED MERCHANT CRUISER   COASTER   MOTOR VESSEL   SUBMARINE   TANKER

Top: In 1939 the Marine and Coastwatching Service was established. It created 83 Look Out Posts (LOPs) at 10–20 mile intervals around the coast. Alongside them, 'EIRE' signs were constructed to alert Allied and Axis aircraft that they were over neutral Ireland. The remains of one such sign are still visible today at Malin Head. (Photo Tony Roche)

Bottom: In 1940/41 the *Luftwaffe* bombed counties Louth, Meath, Carlow, Kildare, Wicklow and Wexford, as well as Belfast and Dublin. In one attack 300 buildings were destroyed or damaged, 28 civilians died and 90 were injured when four high-explosive bombs were dropped on the North Strand, Dublin, in May 1941. (Courtesy of the National Library of Ireland)

December 1940 the battle of the Atlantic was fought directly off the coast of Ireland, with the *Kriegsmarine* enjoying frequent successes in operations against Allied convoys, now marshalled through the northwestern approaches. As in 'the Great War', the 250 square miles of ocean off the Donegal coast became 'killing lanes' for Allied shipping, with up to two ships being lost daily from attacks by U-boats and their aerial partners, the Focke Wulf-200 Condors. Conversely, submarine losses in the Atlantic were relatively low in this phase of the war, which would eventually be regarded by U-boat crews as the 'Happy Time' due to the ease and success rate with which U-boats sank Allied vessels. The British Navy was frustrated by limited sonar capability, as well as the tendency for U-boat attacks to take place at night.

Given the scale of the hostilities, it was only a matter of time before Irish vessels were caught up in events. On 1 August 1940 two vessels, the *City of Waterford* and *Kerry Head*, were attacked inside territorial waters off the coast of Cork. The *Kerry Head* (*see* p.135) was the victim of an aerial attack, bombed by a German aircraft southeast of the Old Head of Kinsale. It suffered only minor damage, however, enabling the leaking vessel to make port for repairs. The German Government issued a statement of "sincere regret" at the occurrence and agreed to compensate the owners for any damage incurred. On 22 October the same vessel was less fortunate when it was attacked once again by German aircraft, while en route from Limerick to England in ballast. This time the bombs struck a direct hit on the vessel as it was travelling 4 miles south of Black Ball Head and in sight of Cape Clear, Co. Cork. The crew of 12 perished in the attack. Another Irish vessel, the *Luimneach*, despite displaying 'EIRE' in large

white letters on her sides, was attacked 260 miles south of Kinsale by *U-46* on 4 September. A report in *Lloyd's List* in March 1944 details further losses of Irish vessels during the war, declaring that 16 Irish ships, totalling 30,000 tons and 135 mariners, were lost since the beginning of the war.

Although the general public was largely unaware of the submarine warfare that was being waged in the waters around Ireland, a series of bombing incidents by the *Luftwaffe* in 1940 and 1941 certainly brought home the harsh realities of warfare. Campile, in Wexford, was the first location to be bombed, in August 1940, with the loss of three lives. This was followed in 1941 by bombing attacks in counties Meath, Carlow, Kildare, Wicklow, Wexford and Dublin. Worse was yet to come, however, with the bombing of the North Strand, Dublin, in May 1941 and the tragic loss of 41 innocent civilian lives. Belfast fared far worse, though, when it was intentionally attacked in a massive raid by nearly 200 German bombers in April, resulting in nearly 1,000 deaths and over 1,500 injuries.

As 1941 progressed it became clear that the Allies were steadily improving their techniques for the detection, attack and destruction of the lurking U-boats. In addition, the increased use of Lough Foyle, in Derry, and the adjacent air bases for convoy-protection duties helped reduce the strategic value of the Irish Treaty ports. The breaking of German transmission codes also played a considerable role in curbing the effectiveness of the U-boats. Other factors contributed, too: the loss of experienced U-boat commanders; increased anti-submarine and anti-aircraft operations; and the capture of an enigma machine. All of this meant that the 'Happy Time' of the previous year was over for the U-boat commanders. Constrained by these developments, Admiral Karl Donitz was forced to intercept the convoys further west, out into the Atlantic. With the entry of the USA into the war, the period January–June 1942 saw U-boats sinking large amounts of merchant tonnage in the western North Atlantic, the Caribbean and the Gulf of Mexico, resulting in submarines being absent from Irish waters. This 'Second Happy Time' for German submarine crews was a consequence of American failure to institute a convoy system along the eastern seaboard of the United States.

Now that the European theatre of operations was being given priority, there was a continual build-up of Allied air and naval strength around Ireland through 1942 and 1943, and American forces were deployed in massive numbers in Britain and Northern Ireland. As Allied air cover had improved on both sides of the ocean, the great convoy battles of 1943 were mainly fought in an area of the mid-Atlantic known as 'the Gap', or the Black Pit,

Above: A model of the MV *Kerlogue*, which is best known for the heroic rescues it performed: saving 13 crew from the stricken *Wild Rose* of Liverpool, which sank near Tuskar Rock; and rescuing 164 survivors of three German naval ships, sunk 360 miles SW of Fastnet. (Photo Con Brogan, with permission of the National Maritime Museum, Dún Laoghaire)

Top: Early in the war German U-boat attacks on Allied shipping resulted in the loss of many ships, along with their cargoes, crews and passengers. The implementation of the convoy system resulted in a much safer method of voyage, with the accompanying escort boats employed to protect against and to deter enemy attacks. (Ian Lawler Collection)

Bottom: Despite flying a neutral flag, Ireland's merchant navy did not escape German attentions. The SS *Irish Pine* was torpedoed by *U-608* south of Newfoundland in November 1942, with the loss of all 33 men on board. Painting by Kenneth King. (Courtesy of the National Maritime Museum, Dún Laoghaire)

which was was out of the range of Allied aircraft. The improved air cover had serious consequences for the men of the *Unterseewaffe*, with U-boats increasingly being sunk, especially in waters closer to their French bases. The theatre of operations for the Bay of Biscay, for example, extended northwards to the limits of Irish territorial waters, with the Allies sinking an impressive 65 U-boats in Biscay waters from 1943 to 1944.

It was normal to see Irish merchant vessels in such waters, but the threat of attack was ever present. On 23 October 1943 the 335-ton MV *Kerlogue*, owned by the Wexford Steamship Company and en route to deliver coal to Lisbon, was attacked by two unidentified aircraft approximately 120 miles off Kinsale, Co. Cork. It was subjected to a 25-minute cannon attack, resulting in four casualties on board, including the ship's master. The vessel turned around and headed for Cork. A British inquiry later identified the aircraft as Mosquitoes from RAF 307 Polish Squadron, and accordingly made compensation payments to those injured. In December 1943 the MV *Kerlogue* rescued 168 German sailors in Biscay after their ships had been sunk during a naval engagement with British vessels. Four of the sailors subsequently died on board the *Kerlogue* from injuries sustained during the initial attack or from exposure to the cold Atlantic waters. In contravention of Admiralty instructions, the 164 survivors were landed in Cork and were interned for the duration of the war in the Curragh Internment Camp.

Despite flying a neutral flag, Ireland's merchant navy did not escape German attentions either. The SS *Irish Pine* was torpedoed by *U-608* south of Newfoundland in November 1942, with the loss of all 33 men on board, while the SS *Irish Oak* was torpedoed in the mid-Atlantic on 15 May 1943. Closer to Ireland there were significant attacks on Allied shipping. The largest single shipping casualty of the war occurred off Malin Head, Co. Donegal, on 26 October 1940. The *Empress of Britain* (42,348 tons), en route from Capetown, South Africa, was bombed by a single German aircraft (*see* p.137). She burned fiercely for two days and was eventually sunk with a torpedo from *U-32* while under tow. Although carrying few passengers, she was said to have been carrying a large consignment of gold and silver. In September 1944 the *Empire Heritage* (*see* p.146), bound for Liverpool and sailing with convoy HXF-305, was attacked twice with torpedoes by *U-482*, under the command of *Kapitänleutnant* Hartmut Graf von Matuschka, killing 103 of her crew and servicemen. The wreck site of the *Empire Heritage* is littered with the trucks and Sherman tanks that were part of the vessel's cargo, making it an attractive wreck for divers to visit.

By the end of 1943 it was becoming apparent that the threat to convoys on the western approaches was considerably reduced as combined air and sea operations limited the freedom of U-boats in the Atlantic waters. Yet the threat never entirely disappeared and Allied aircraft increased operations along the south and south-western coastline of Ireland between January and March 1944, following intelligence that U-boats had begun to steer closer to Ireland in an effort to locate convoys. As the German submarines closed in on the west coast of Ireland, 15 U-boats were sunk in January, followed by 20 in February. Such missions were not without peril for the Allied aircrews, too. On 27 February 1944 an American Liberator H/110 on anti-submarine patrol flew into the Great Skellig Rock as it coasted below 150m to avoid contact with U-boat radar. In April 1944, Operation CORK was commenced in the Irish Sea, Celtic Sea and the western approaches, to tackle the potential threat posed by U-boats to the planned invasion of Normandy. This operation involved 30 aircraft patrolling 20,000 square miles of water and making complete radar sweeps of the entire area every 30 minutes. It was supposed to prevent U-boats from entering the invasion zone, but it proved only a minor success in harassing enemy submarines: 40 U-boats were mustered to attack Allied shipping off the coast of Devon and Cornwall in the week after D-Day.

The waters around Ireland remained relatively quiet in the months following the opening of the Second Front, with the ports in Northern Ireland no longer serving an immediate strategic importance. The capture of U-boat bases in France also meant that by the autumn, the transatlantic convoys could now be rerouted in relative safety to the south of Ireland. Despite the best efforts of the German navy, Britain was never again to be threatened with the spectre of starvation, as was the case in World War I. Clearly, U-boats did not have the same freedom of movement in Irish coastal waters and for this reason the bulk of the shipping losses in this conflict occurred further from the coast than those in the previous war. Yet between November 1944 and April 1945 there was a significant increase in attacks on merchant shipping and a reduction in U-boat losses. This was partly due to a new type of *schnorchel* (a device enabling fresh air to be taken into a submarine and fumes to be expelled when using diesel engines while submerged), which allowed for greater periods of time underwater. A new submarine, the Type XXI, which was powered by electromotors, also allowed crews to remain underwater for virtually most of the operation, making them very difficult to detect by the Allies using radar and ASDIC sonar devices. However,

Above: U-boats berthed at Lisahally, Co. Derry, an embarkation point for the disposal of U-boats between the months of November 1945 and February 1946 as part of 'Operation Deadlight'. In total, 116 German U-boats were towed from Lisahally and Loch Ryan in Scotland to the northern approaches, where they were deliberately sunk. (Courtesy of the Royal Navy Submarine Museum)

most submarines of this type failed to emerge from training or from shipyards, with only a single example attaining operational status before the war ended. This was *U-2511* (*see* p.166), which was scuttled off the Donegal coast after the war.

In the closing weeks of the war a number of engagements took place in Irish waters. On 23 March the *U-1003* was scuttled 10 miles north of Inishtrahull, Co. Donegal, after being rammed by the Canadian frigate HMCS *New Glasgow* and depth-charged by other Canadian vessels. On 8 April HMS *Fitzroy* and HMS *Byron* sank *U-1001* off the Fastnet Rock, Co. Cork, and on 12 April *U-1024* was sunk in the central Irish Sea. On 21 April *U-636* was attacked and sunk 100 miles northwest of Arranmore, Co. Donegal. Despite new technologies, weary and inexperienced U-boat crews were unable to overcome the strength of Allied air and naval forces that were ranged against them. As the war was drawing to a close, Admiral Donitz ordered all U-boats to cease hostilities on 4 May 1945, resulting in the surrender of 154 U-boats to Allied forces. The German *Kriegsmarine* had suffered the loss

of 30,000 of their 40,000 submariners during the war. Of the 700 U-boats sunk during hostilities, it is estimated that approximately 60 were lost in the waters surrounding Ireland. This contrasts somewhat to World War I figures, with around 15 U-boats lost out of a fleet of 185.

At the last combined meeting of the Allied leaders, the Potsdam Conference (16 July–2 August 1945), it was decided that a small number of U-boats would be distributed among the victors for the purposes of research and training, with the remaining vessels to be sunk in deep waters in an exercise known as 'Operation Deadlight'. As part of Deadlight, 116 U-boats were to be scuttled in the Rockall Trough, 120 miles northwest of the Donegal coast. Both Lisahally, on Lough Foyle in Co. Derry, and Loch Ryan in Scotland were used as embarkation points for the disposal of these submarines. Between the months of November 1945 and February 1946, the 116 German U-boats were towed into the northern approaches and sunk by various means. It was decided to carry out live fire practice, with a number of U-boats to be used as air or submarine targets. The remainder were to be sunk by demolition charges installed by naval specialists. However, only half (58) of the U-boats were scuttled in the designated area. The task proved more difficult than anticipated as warships were unsuitable for towing, unmanned submarines were difficult to tow and the weather conditions were very poor given that it was

Above: Various German submarine officers, including *Oberleutnant zur See* Klaus Hilgendorf, commander of *U-1009* (*centre*), boarding a train at Derry after surrendering in May 1945. (Courtesy of the Royal Navy Submarine Museum)

mid-winter. Tow-lines parted en route to the designated dumpsite, leaving little option in many cases but to use gunfire to sink the unmanned U-boats where they sat. Even when submarines were towed to their designated resting place, the elaborate charges could not be detonated, so the majority had to be sunk by gunfire, with only a few being sunk by aircraft or submarines as originally planned.

During the war, people living on the Irish coastline observed aerial dogfights, heavily escorted convoys passing along the coastline, bodies washing up on seashores and mines exploding on beaches. Yet for all the destruction and loss that had been wrought for six long years in the battle of the Atlantic, the population of Ireland was largely unaware of the war that was being waged in their coastal waters. The years of 'the Emergency' saw heavy censorship of newspapers, newsreels and radio broadcasts to minimise coverage of events that would be seen to favour one side or the other, and this distanced the bulk of the population from the ebb and flow of war. Given the country's non-belligerent status and a continued policy of neutrality throughout the Cold War, it is not surprising that Ireland's maritime war heritage remains largely overlooked. This has been remedied somewhat by the marine, dive and

seabed mapping surveys (INSS and INFOMAR) carried out by the GSI and the Marine Institute of Ireland, the UAU and, of course, by the boundless energy of divers around this island. Such work has led to the discovery of over 30 previously unknown U-boat wrecks off the Donegal coast, throwing light on an important aspect of both Irish and international history that is being increasingly appreciated.

As with the wrecks of World War I, these vessels give dramatic witness to events that were happening on our doorstep. While many Irish people lost their lives in the conflict, it is only through the preservation and study of wrecks such as these that the reality of the events of the time is highlighted and understood. While the wrecks of World War I will soon be protected under the 100-year rule, there is a real need to identify the more important sites from World War II in our waters and to afford them the protection that the National Monuments Acts allow. The awareness and appreciation of this important aspect of our maritime heritage by the diving community will play a critical part in the preservation of wrecks for future generations.

Following pages: Irish merchant shipping displayed the Irish tricolour and EIRE sign on their decks and hulls during WWII. Nonetheless many Irish ships were attacked, with 149 lives lost in total. The *Kerry Head* was sunk, with the loss of its 12 crew, after being attacked by a German aircraft. Painting by Kenneth King. (Courtesy of the National Maritime Museum, Dún Laoghaire)

KENNETH KING

Athenia

GSI ref. code	112
NMS wreck no.	W07146
Location	388km NW of Erris Head, Co. Mayo
Co-ordinates	56 44 20.90N, 014 22 30.40W
Depth of water	189m
Vessel type	Liner
Vessel dimensions	164m (l), 20m (b), 8.4m (d)
Date of building	1923
Date of loss	3 September 1939

Circumstances of loss

The *Athenia* holds the dubious honour of being the first victim of submarine warfare in World War II. Hostilities between Britain and Germany were only a few hours old when the *Athenia* was attacked without warning on 3 September 1939, some 250 miles west of Inishtrahull Island, Co. Donegal. The commander of *U-30*, Fritz-Julius Lemp, mistakenly identified the liner as an armed merchant cruiser. The attack went against the Hague Convention and the Prize Rules, under which merchant ships of a belligerent state could not be sunk without warning, and only after the crew and passengers had been safely removed from the vessel. Germany denied responsibility for the sinking, claiming that no U-boats were in the area at the time and that the *Athenia* was most likely lost as a result of hitting a British mine. Further efforts to cover up Germany's involvement led to Britain being blamed for torpedoing or planting a bomb on the *Athenia* in an attempt to draw the USA into the war on Britain's side.

Below: The 13,581-ton passenger liner *Athenia* had already left Glasgow for Montreal with 1,103 passengers when war was declared between Britain and Germany. The Donaldson Atlantic Line-owned liner was attacked without warning. It was the first ship to be sunk by a German submarine in WWII. (Ian Lawler Collection)

The *Athenia* was a 13,581-ton, twin-screw passenger liner owned by the Donaldson Atlantic Line. It was built in 1923 by the Fairfield Shipbuilding and Engineering Co., Glasgow, and was capable of 15.5 knots. It was a large vessel with two masts and one funnel. At the time of the attack the liner, under Captain James Cook, was en route from Glasgow to Montreal, stopping at Liverpool and Belfast to take on passengers. It carried 1,000 tons of cargo, along with 315 crew and 1,103 passengers, 311 of this number being American citizens. On the evening of 3 September a single torpedo hit the port side, behind the engine-room, resulting in all power to the ship being lost. The vessel listed heavily, making the launch of lifeboats quite difficult. One lifeboat, crowded with people, fell from the davits and threw all its occupants into the sea. Another capsized some time later and a third ran foul of the propellers of a rescue vessel when coming alongside. A number of vessels responded to the vessel's distress call: the Norwegian steamship *Knute Nelson* rescued 430 people; a Swedish yacht rescued 50 people; while the British destroyers HMS *Electra* and *Escort* rescued about 500. Despite the speedy evacuation and rescue of passengers and crew, 128 people were lost, mostly to the torpedo attack itself. The survivors were landed at Galway, Halifax in Canada and Greenock in Scotland. The *Athenia* took 14 hours to sink.

On the seafloor

The wreck of the *Athenia* measures 139m in length, 29m in width and 19.3m in maximum height, with an average height of 9.8m. The vessel is orientated NE–SW on the seafloor. Sediment scouring has occurred around the vessel. The vessel sits in deep water far offshore, making resolution by multibeam sonar relatively poor.

Printed Sources

Bonsor 1979, Vol. iii, 346

Hocking 1989, 56-7

Larn & Larn 2002

Smith 1947, 46

Williams 1997, 86-7

Woodman 2004, 11-19

Internet Source

www.uboat.net

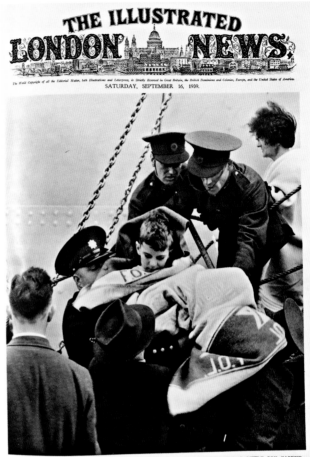

Above: The *Illustrated London News* shows survivors of the *Athenia* being helped ashore by gardaí and army personnel at Galway. The sinking of the passenger liner by the *U-30* within hours of war being declared aroused fears that the Nazi authorities would conduct an unrestricted submarine campaign, similar to that in WWI. (Courtesy of the National Library of Ireland)

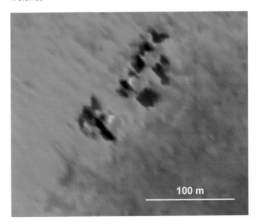

Above: Wreck of the *Athenia* lying on the seabed, 388km NW of Mayo. The remains of the vessel sit in deep water, making it difficult to obtain high-resolution multibeam imagery of the wreck.

FV Thomas Hankins

GSI ref. code	115
NMS wreck no.	W07682
Location	2.2km NW of Tory Island, off the coast of Co. Donegal
Co-ordinates	55 23 09.53N, 008 32 54.35W
Depth of water	96m
Vessel type	Fishing trawler
Vessel dimensions	38m (l), 7m (b), 4m (d)
Date of building	1918
Date of loss	20 November 1939

Circumstances of loss

The *Thomas Hankins* was a 274-ton trawler built in 1918 by J.P. Reynoldson & Sons Ltd., South Shields. It was initially owned by the Pembroke Hake Fishing Co. (E.V. Pennington), of London, before being acquired by the Boston Deep Sea Fishing & Ice Co., based in Fleetwood, Lancashire. On 20 November 1939, at 10.30am, the trawler was shelled by *U-33*, under the command of *Kapitänleutnant* Hans-Wilhelm von Dresky, 14 miles northwest of Donegal. The *U-33* went on to sink two other vessels that day: the *Delphine*, 18 miles NNE of Tory Island at 4.00pm; and the *Sea Sweeper*, 25 miles WNW of Tory at 5.05pm. In each instance the sinking was achieved using shells from the U-boat's deck gun. The crew of the *Thomas Hankins* (Master M. Hankins and 11 others) escaped on a lifeboat, but not before the U-boat commander had shouted to the crew of the trawler to check that they were alright. They were rescued by another Fleetwood trawler, the *Esher*, after ten hours on the lifeboat and landed in Moville, Co. Donegal. They reported that the ship had been shelled without warning, the second shell penetrating the bows and the fifth penetrating the boiler, causing the trawler to sink after about 25 minutes.

On the seafloor

The wreck of the *Thomas Hankins* appears to be badly broken up and spread out over the seabed for a length of 54m. It has a maximum height of 6.8m above the seabed, with an average height of 3m.

Printed Sources
BVLS 1939–1945, 56
Larn & Larn 2002
UKHO Wreck Data 1996

Internet Sources
www.fleetwood-trawlers.info
www.float-trawlers.lancashire.gov.uk
(Fleetwood Online Archive of Trawlers)
www.uboat.net

Above: Multibeam view of the badly broken-up wreck on the seafloor.

Left: Photo of the 274-ton trawler in 1919, en route to fishing grounds. (Courtesy of the National Maritime Museum, Greenwich)

HMS Carinthia

GSI ref. code	131
NMS wreck no.	W07682
Location	65km WNW of Bloody Foreland, Co. Donegal
Co-ordinates	55 14 51.04N, 009 17 58.96W
Depth of water	112m
Vessel type	Armed merchant cruiser
Vessel dimensions	183m (l), 22.5m (b), 12.4 (d)
Date of building	1925
Date of loss	7 June 1940

Circumstances of loss

The *Carinthia*, formerly known as the *Servia*, was a 20,277-ton steel steamship owned by the Cunard White Star Line and built in 1925 by Vickers Armstrong, of Barrow-in-Furness. It was propelled by eight-cylinder, triple-expansion steam turbines capable of attaining 18 knots in speed and could carry 1,650 passengers in three classes. She was one of a class of five ships built for Cunard to operate on transatlantic routes, the others being the *Scythia*, *Samaria*, *Laconia* and *Franconia*. During the 1930s the *Carinthia* was also engaged in cruising.

When the hostilities broke out in September 1939, the vessel was commissioned as an armed merchant crusier, equipped with eight 6-inch and two 3-inch deck guns, under the command of Captain J.F.B. Barrett. On

7 June 1940, while on patrol on the western approaches, she was torpedoed by *U-46* under the command of *Kapitänleutnant* Engelbert Endrass. The stricken vessel remained afloat long enough to allow the evacuation of the crew, except for two officers and two ratings who were killed in the initial attack. She was towed by escorting vessels for Glasgow, but eventually sank off the coast of Donegal.

On the seafloor

The wreck of the *Carinthia* measures 169m in length, 38m in width and 10m in maximum height, with an average height of 7.6m. It is orientated roughly E–W. For the observant diver, patches of grey paint on the side of the hull would suggest the wreck is fairly recent, rather than 70 years old, and on that basis might be expected to be fairly intact. However, the whole ship has concertinaed over to starboard and collapsed down, deck upon deck, so that the wreckage sits only 8m high in its entirety. All of the glass in the portholes on the port side of the vessel is smashed, which suggests that it was depth-charged and this, combined with the ravages of the Atlantic swells, might account for her devastated condition. The end result of this collapse is that the deck has a list of about 35 degrees. Her bow is twisted off somewhat and her forward bow

Below: The RMS *Carinthia*, photographed passing Sydney Harbour Bridge during a world cruise in February 1933. (Ian Lawler Collection)

Above: The comfortable surrounds of the 'smoking room' on the RMS *Carinthia*. (Ian Lawler Collection)

Above: Official Cunard White Star Line postcard showing the rather chic-looking 'Soda Fountain' bar on the RMS *Carinthia*. (Ian Lawler Collection)

area and the 6-inch guns have slewed to point aft. Most of the mid-ships upper decks are gone, leaving a clean 'deck' area across the ship, around and aft of what was the bridge area. Further aft, as the wreck drops to the stern area, a huge dark void can be seen like a 'window' inside the hull, and even the strongest diver's torch cannot make out any decks inside this void, which means most of them must have collapsed internally. It presents an eerie, uninviting darkness in 112m of sea water. The port side of her stern stands up well, to about 10m, whereas the starboard side is level with the seabed.

Printed Sources
Hocking 1989, 123
Larn & Larn 2002
McGill 2010, 74–7
Williams 1997, 99–100

Internet Source
www.uboat.net

Above: Multibeam overview of the 169m-long wreck on the seafloor. Even though the wreck is in poor condition and broken up, its outline is clearly visible.

Top: Official Cunard White Star Line postcard of the RMS *Carinthia* in Cork harbour, with the Catholic cathedral of Cobh visible in the background. The postcard was painted by James S. Mann (1883–1946). (Courtesy of the National Monuments Service, DAHG)

Bottom: The detached bow of the HMS *Carinthia* lies listing to its starboard side, with the port anchor still in its hawse. (Photo Barry McGill)

HMS Transylvania

GSI ref. code	23
NMS wreck no.	W07688
Location	54km NW of Malin Head, Co. Donegal
Co-ordinates	55 48 43.31N, 007 48 40.90W
Depth of water	129m
Vessel type	Armed Merchant Cruiser
Vessel dimensions	168m (l), 21m (b), 12m (d)
Date of building	1925
Date of loss	10 August 1940

Circumstances of loss

The *Transylvania* was a 16,923-ton steel steamship built in 1925 by the Fairfield Shipbuilding & Engineering Co. of Glasgow. It was originally owned by the Anchor Line (Henderson Brothers, Glasgow) and employed as a liner on the transatlantic crossing between Glasgow and New York. The vessel was propelled by steam turbine engines capable of producing speeds up to 17 knots. It had made numerous transatlantic crossings before being requisitioned by the Admiralty in August 1939. It was converted into an auxiliary cruiser, armed with eight 6-inch deck guns

and renamed HMS *Transylvania*. While on patrol in the early hours of 10 August 1940, under the command of Captain F.N. Miles, the *Transylvania* was torpedoed by *U-56* (captained by Otto Harms). The HMS *Transylvania* was one of two ships sunk by *U-56* off the Donegal coast: six days earlier SS *Boma* had been torpedoed and sunk while travelling in convoy OB-193. The *U-56* sunk four ships in total during the war, totalling 25,783 tons of shipping. Following the torpedo attack, the badly damaged *Transylvania* was taken in tow, but later sank. Some 300 of her crew were rescued by trawlers, assisted by HMS *Ashanti*, as the task of launching lifeboats was extremely hazardous owing to rough sea conditions. Two officers and two ratings lost their lives during the attack.

On the seafloor

The wreck of the *Transylvania* measures 182m in length, 27m in width and 11.6m in height, with an average height of 7.7m. The vessel is orientated WNW–ESE on the seafloor. A small scour has developed at her east end, and

Below: Postcard of the *Transylvania* on one of its transatlantic voyages prior to WWII. The British liner could carry 279 first-class passengers, 344 second-class passengers and 800 third-class passengers. (Ian Lawler Collection)

Above: The SS *Transylvania* at anchor in port. It was originally employed as a liner on the transatlantic crossing between Glasgow and New York. Early in WWII it was requisitioned by the British Admiralty and converted to an auxiliary cruiser. (Ian Lawler Collection)

Right: Multibeam view of the wreck, which lies almost upright on the seabed in 129m of water.

the wreck appears to be upright with a slight list to port. The bow is to the WNW. Risdon Beazley Marine Ltd. dived the wreck in 1969 and located the torpedo hole on the starboard side, abreast no. 2 hold. Lying on her port side with an estimated list of 30 degrees, this wreck is not for the faint-hearted diver as she lies in 129m of water. The most impressive aspect of the wreck is its sheer size, but practically all of the structure above deck level has apparently been wiped away, leaving an almost featureless slope with her guns still in place. Two 6-inch guns stand sentinel on either side of the deck area, just before the bow, and form one of the most impressive sights in deep wreck diving.

Printed Sources

Bishop 2010, 24–8
BVLS 1939–1945, 5
Hocking 1989, 712
Larn & Larn 2002

McGill 2010, 74-7
UKHO Wreck Data
Williams 1997, 108
Wynn 1997, Vol. i, 40

Cumberland

GSI ref. code	109
NMS wreck no.	W07241
Location	10km N of Inishtrahull Island, Co. Donegal
Co-ordinates	55 31 33.13N, 007 15 13.32W
Depth of water	55m
Vessel type	Cargo vessel
Vessel dimensions	158m (l), 19.5m (b), 11m (d)
Date of building	1919
Date of loss	24 August 1940

Circumstances of loss

This steam merchant cargo ship was built by Bremer Vulkan Schiffsbau, Vegesack, Germany, in 1919 and was originally known as the *Wendland*. It was transferred to Britain in 1921, as part of war reparations agreed in the Treaty of Versailles, and was renamed the *Cumberland* after being purchased by the Federal Steam Navigation Co. of London. The vessel displaced 10,939 tons and was powered by 1,270 horsepower, triple-expansion engines, giving it a maximum speed of 14 knots. When lost, the *Cumberland* was under the command of Edwin A.J. Williams and was en route from Glasgow, via Liverpool, to Curaçao, Panama and Dunedin, New Zealand, with 9,000 tons of metal and general cargo.

The *Cumberland* was travelling in a convoy of 32 ships (OB-202), escorted by two anti-submarine trawlers, two destroyers and a corvette, when it was sighted by *U-57*. It was close to midnight on 23 August 1940, 25 miles northeast of Malin Head, when the attack occurred. The *U-57* fired a single torpedo at the *St. Dunstan*, the lead ship in the convoy, striking its starboard side. Minutes later the *Cumberland* was also hit on its starboard side, causing the deaths of four crew. The passenger liner *Havildar* was hit next, but managed to stay afloat; it was towed to the Clyde the following day. The *U-57*, which was under the command of *Oberleutnant zur See* Erich Topp, managed to slip away unnoticed and even sank another ship, from convoy HX-65, on its return to Bergen. The 54 surviving crew of the *Cumberland* abandoned the sinking ship and were landed at Moville, Co. Donegal. The vessel stayed afloat and drifted for 12 hours, before eventually sinking

Below: The *Cumberland* docked at the quayside in 1936. (Courtesy of the National Maritime Museum, Greenwich)

Above: Bollards on the wreck of the *Cumberland*. (Photo Barry McGill)

into the depths 10km north of Inishtrahull Island, Co. Donegal.

On the seafloor

The wreck of the *Cumberland* is orientated WNW–ESE on the seabed and measures 152m long and 33m wide, with a maximum height of 8.1m. In 1981 the wreck was reported to be largely intact, with its funnel still standing, but extensive salvage over the years and the ravages of the north Atlantic swell have taken their toll on the remains of the vessel. Despite this, the wreck is still substantially intact amidships, with the hull rising up over 5m from the seabed. The fore and aft holds have been completely torn open, however, and their contents now lie strewn across the seafloor. The *Cumberland* had been carrying cargo outward bound for New Zealand and all manner of goods can be seen, including corrugated iron, plate glass, rolls of linoleum, cutlery, ceramic electrical insulators and china of all qualities, up to high-grade porcelain made by Royal Doulton. The white china and the insulators are particularly prominent, strewn around on the seabed. Aft the stern, the twin screws and engines are still fairly intact and are well worth a look.

Printed Sources
Hocking 1989, 172
Larn & Larn 2002
UKHO Wreck Data 1996
Wynn 1997, Vol. ii, 41

Internet Source
www.uboat.net

Above: A 3D, multibeam image of the *Cumberland* lying on the seabed.

City of Simla

GSI ref. code	6
NMS wreck no.	W07230
Location	78km NW of Malin Head, Co. Donegal
Co-ordinates	55 56 9.96N, 008 9 53.46W
Depth of water	175m
Vessel type	Cargo vessel
Vessel dimensions	145m (l), 18m (b), 12m (d)
Date of building	1921
Date of loss	21 September 1940

Circumstances of loss

The *City of Simla* was a 10,138-ton, steel merchant steamship of Glasgow, owned by Ellerman Lines. It was built by W. Gray Co. Ltd. of West Hartlepool in 1921 and was propelled by four steam turbine engines, giving it a maximum speed of 13.5 knots. On the day it was sunk, the vessel was en route from London to Cape Town and Bombay, under the command of Herbert Percival, and carrying 183 crew, 167 passengers and 3,000 tons of general cargo. It was one of 27 vessels in convoy OB-216, being escorted by one escort ship, one sloop, three corvettes and one destroyer. At approximately 2.00am on 21 September the vessel was attacked and sunk by *U-138*, commanded by *Oberleutnant zur See* Wolfgang Lüth. Two passengers, including a 17-year-old boy, and one crew member were killed by the explosion when the torpedo hit the stern. The remaining crew and passengers abandoned the crippled vessel. Of those, 318 were picked up by the SS *Guinean* and later transferred to the destroyer HMS

Vanquisher, while a Belgian trawler rescued 17 crew and 12 passengers. The badly damaged *City of Simla* sank a day later. In all, four ships from convoy OB-216 were sunk by *U-138* off the coast of Donegal over a two-day period, including the *Boka* (eight dead), the *New Sevilla* (two dead) and the *Empire Adventure* (21 dead).

On the seafloor

The wreck of the *City of Simla* was located in 1969 by Risdon Beazley Marine Ltd., and was to be found lying upside-down on the seabed with its stern blown off. The vessel is orientated NW–SE on the seafloor and measures 107m in length, 29m in width and has a maximum height of 20m above the seabed.

Printed Sources

Hocking 1989, 147

Larn & Larn 2002

UKHO Wreck Data 1996

Williams 1997, 112

Wynn 1997, Vol. ii, 112

Internet Source

www.uboat.net

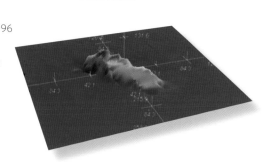

Above: A 3D, multibeam image of the *City of Simla*, which lies upside-down with its stern blown. Further damage was done to the wreck as a result of salvage work carried out in the 1960s.

Below: Postcard of the 10,138-ton merchant ship. (Courtesy of the National Monuments Service)

Kerry Head

Above: The ill-fated *Kerry Head*, which was attacked by a German aircraft, despite displaying the tricolour and 'EIRE' sign prominently on her decks. Neutral status couldn't save the ship and her 12-man crew. Painting by Kenneth King. (Courtesy of the National Maritime Museum, Dún Laoghaire)

GSI ref. code	233
NMS wreck no.	W08492
Location	*c.* 15km NW of Mizen Head, Co. Cork
Co-ordinates	51 29 53.56N, 010 01 28.24W
Depth of water	69m
Vessel type	Coaster
Vessel dimensions	59m (l), 9.5m (b), 3.5m (d)
Date of building	1913
Date of loss	22 October 1940

Circumstances of loss

This 825-ton steam coaster was built in 1913 by John Fullerton & Co., Paisley, and was originally called SS *Eurus*. It had triple-expansion engines, which were constructed by Ross & Duncan. The first owner was Gregory B. Wadworth of Goole, then it was purchased by Mrs E. Wadsworth and C.P. Wadsworth in 1921. The Side Shipping Co. (Connell & Grace) of Newcastle purchased the vessel in 1922 and renamed it *Simonside*. In 1926 it was renamed the *Kerry Head* after being acquired by its final owners, W.T. Herriot (Mullock & Son) of Limerick.

The *Kerry Head* was attacked early in the war when, on 1 August 1940, it was bombed by a German aircraft southeast of the Old Head of Kinsale. In that attack it suffered only minor damage, enabling the leaking vessel to make port for repairs. The German government issued a statement of "sincere regret" at the occurrence and agreed to compensate the owners for any damage incurred. On 22 October the vessel was not so fortunate when it was attacked by German aircraft while en route from Limerick to England, in ballast. This time the bombs struck a direct hit on the vessel as it was travelling 4 miles south of Black Ball Head and in sight of Cape Clear, Co. Cork. The crew of 12 perished in the attack.

On the seafloor

The wreck of the *Kerry Head* measures 52m in length, 25m in width and 2m in maximum height, with an average height of 1m. The vessel appears to be badly broken up and is orientated N–S on the seafloor. There is a deep sediment scour to the east of the wreck.

Printed Sources
Hocking 1969, 381
Larn & Larn 2002

The Irish Times, 7 September 1940;
29 October 1940; 2 November
1940; 1 March 1941
UKHO Wreck Data 1996

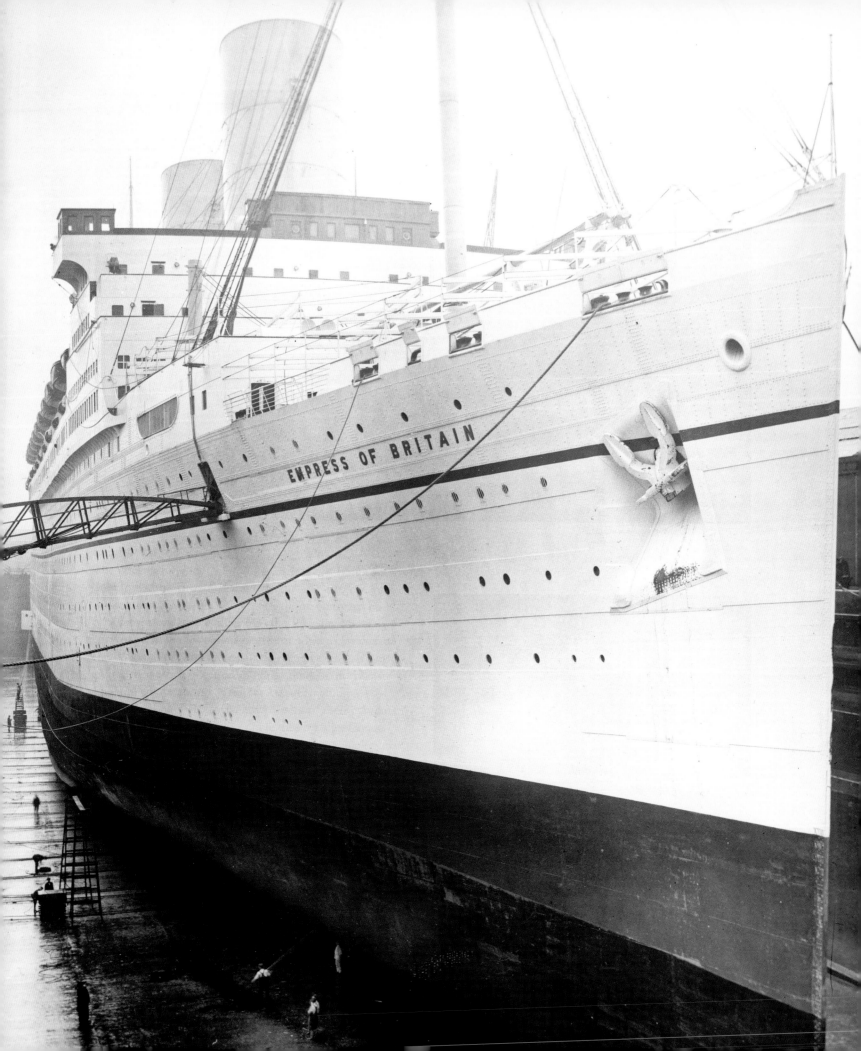

Empress of Britain

GSI ref. code	1
NMS wreck no.	W07307
Location	90km WNW of Bloody Foreland, Co. Donegal
Co-ordinates	55 19 3.58N, 009 40 57.72W
Depth of water	159m
Vessel type	Passenger Liner
Vessel dimensions	231m (l), 30m (b), 10m (d)
Date of building	1931
Date of loss	28 October 1940

At 42,348 tons, this passenger liner was the largest vessel of the Canadian Pacific Railway Company fleet and was the largest merchant vessel lost during World War II. It was built by John Brown & Co., Glasgow, in 1931 at a phenomenal cost of $15,000,000 and was considered to be one of the most luxurious vessels of its time. It embarked on its first world cruise in 1933 and could travel up to a

Opposite: Built at a cost of $15,000,000 and weighing 42,348 tons, the *Empress of Britain* was the largest merchant vessel to be lost during WWII. The breathtaking scale of the liner can be fully appreciated when viewed in dry dock. (Courtesy of the National Maritime Museum, Greenwich)

speed of 24 knots, with accommodation for 423 first-class passengers, 260 tourist-class passengers and 470 third-class passengers. With the commencement of hostilities in 1939, the liner was requisitioned as a troop transport and it made several voyages for that purpose.

Under the command of Charles Havard Sapsworth, the *Empress of Britain* was on a circuitous voyage from Cape Town via the Suez Canal to Canada and then on to Liverpool when on 26 October 1940, as it was travelling 150 miles off the coast of Ireland, it was attacked by a German long-range Focke-Wulf 200 Condor airplane. The liner was attacked three times and quickly caught fire, killing a number of people on board. The ship did not sink immediately, which enabled most of the 419 crew and 224 military personnel and families to safely board the lifeboats. The survivors were picked up by Royal Navy escorts. The *Empress of Britain* was then taken in tow by a Polish destroyer, the *Burza*, and later assisted by Royal Navy tugs *Marauder* and *Thames*. Two days later, approximately 90km WNW of Bloody Foreland, *Kapitänleutnant* Hans Jenisch in *U-32* torpedoed the *Empress of Britain* twice,

Below: Postcard of the *Empress of Britain* steaming through the Panama Canal during one of her round-the-world trips. (Ian Lawler Collection)

Top: The 'Knickerbocker Bar' on board the *Empress of Britain*.
(Ian Lawler Collection)

Bottom: The 'Olympian Pool' on the *Empress of Britain*. The liner was
considered one of the more luxurious vessels of its time when it
embarked on its first world cruise in 1933. (Ian Lawler Collection)

Above: The Focke-Wulf 200 Condor was known as the 'scourge of the Atlantic' due to its success rate in damaging and sinking Allied ships. After suffering an attack by a long-range Focke-Wulf 200 Condor airplane, the *Empress of Britain* was sunk two days later by *U-32*, 90km WNW of Bloody Foreland, Co. Donegal. (Ian Lawler Collection)

causing it to sink in nine minutes. In total, 49 people were lost during the attacks. Two days later, *U-32* was itself sunk by the destroyer HMS *Harvester*.

On the seafloor

The wreck of the *Empress of Britain* measures 212m in length, 40m in width and 23.1m in maximum height, with an average height of 7.1m. The vessel is orientated E–W and lies upside-down on the flat seabed.

Above: Multibeam view of the wreck of the *Empress of Britain* lying in 159m of water.

Printed Sources

Hocking 1989, 222
Larn & Larn 2002
Smith 1947, 83
Williams 1997, 113–14

Internet Source

www.thegreatoceanliners.com

Veronica

GSI ref. code	80
NMS wreck no.	W07834
Location	37km NW of Tory Island, off the coast of Co. Donegal
Co-ordinates	55 31 20.1N, 008 38 44.63W
Depth of water	91m
Vessel type	Merchant vessel
Vessel dimensions	72.5m (l), 11.6m (b), 4.9m (d)
Date of building	1918
Date of loss	17 November 1940

Circumstances of loss

The *Veronica* was a 1,316-ton Swedish merchant steamship, built in 1918 by Limhamn's Skeppsvarv A/B and owned by Rederi-A/B Activ (Joh. Gorthon), Helsingborg. The vessel was en route to Barrow-in-Furness from Aguilas, Spain, with convoy HG-46, under the command of Master R. Elmquist. The *Veronica* was carrying a crew of 20 and an 1,800-ton cargo of iron ore when *U-137*, under the command of *Kapitänleutnant* Herbert Wohlfarth, torpedoed the steamship without warning, sinking it. There were 20 crew on board, and 17 lost their lives in the attack. The remaining survivors were rescued by a fishing vessel after spending five days on a raft and thereafter were landed at Derry. Another vessel in the convoy, the MV *Saint Germain*, was also sunk that day. In previous days the *U-137* had sunk the SS *Cape St Andrew* and the SS *Planter*.

On the seafloor

The *Veronica* is well broken up and is spread out on the seabed over a length of 65m and a width of 13.5m. It has a maximum height of 4.3m and is dominated amidships by the two boilers. Aft following the shaft tunnel leads to the propeller and what appears to be the wheel from an emergency steering position. Forward, a mast lies across the starboard gunwale with a very flat area of wreckage leading to the bow.

Printed Sources
Hocking 1989, 736
Wynn 1997, Vol. i, 112

Internet Source
www.uboat.net

Above: Multibeam image of the broken-up remains of SS *Veronica* on the seabed, at a depth of 97m.

Below: The 1,316-ton Swedish merchant vessel under steam, carrying a cargo of timber. This photo was taken some time before 1932. (Courtesy of the National Maritime Museum, Greenwich)

Bussum (after part)

GSI ref. code	178
NMS wreck no.	W09503
Location	60km NNE of Tory Island, off the coast of Co. Donegal
Co-ordinates	55 48 05.80N, 008 04 32.16W (after part)
Depth of water	131m
Vessel type	Merchant vessel
Vessel dimensions	109.7m (l), 14.6m (b), 6.7m (d)
Date of building	1917
Date of loss	23 November 1940

Circumstances of loss

Early in the war, German U-boat attacks on Allied shipping resulted in the loss of many ships with their cargoes, crews and passengers. Travelling in convoy was regarded as a safer method of voyage, with the accompanying escort boats employed to protect against and deter enemy attacks. This did not always guarantee safety, however, as illustrated by the experience of convoy SC-11. On 22/23 November it was subjected to a devastating attack by U-100, with the loss of seven ships, including the *Bussum*, totalling over 24,601 tons and the tragic loss of 119 lives.

The *Bussum* was a 3,636-ton Dutch steam freighter, built in 1917 by L. Vuijk & Zonen in Capelle aan Den Ijssel and owned by Stoomvaart Maatschappij Oostzee (A. Vinke & Co), Amsterdam. In March 1918 the *Bussum* was requisitioned by the US Government and used as a cargo transport until the end of the war, after which it was returned to its Dutch owners. The *Bussum* narrowly escaped being sunk early in World War II after it was bombed by a German aircraft in the North Sea on 13 May 1940. Although the freighter was damaged and had to be towed to London, it was quickly repaired and returned to service in July. Later that year, on 20 October, the *Bussum* again narrowly escaped disaster when attacked by a U-boat while en route from North Shields to Montreal. Luckily for the *Bussum*, the torpedo attack narrowly missed the stern of the ship and subsequent rounds fired by the U-boat also missed their target. The vessel was able to fend off the U-boat using its 4-inch gun and smokefloats.

As was so often the case at sea, the *Bussum's* luck eventually ran out a few weeks later when the convoy it was travelling with, SC-11, was attacked. In the early hours of 23 November, U-100, under the command of *Kapitänleutnant* Joachim Schepke, encountered and sank six ships within a few hours, with the loss of 83 lives. Later that evening, U-100 used its last remaining torpedo to hit the *Bussum* in the bow, causing it to sink along with its 5,200-ton cargo of grain. The master of the freighter, Lubbert Wulp, and his 28 crew members got off the ship safely and were rescued by the Canadian destroyer HMCS *Ottawa*. The U-100 was itself sunk in March 1941, after being rammed while on patrol to the southeast of Iceland. Only six of the 44 submariners on board survived the fatal blow.

On the seafloor

The wreck lies in two parts, which are reported to be anywhere between 600m and 1.2km apart. Risdon Beazley Marine Ltd located and dived both sections in 1969 and again in 1975. The stern gun of the after part of the *Bussum* was still standing and the cargo of grain was still visible at that time. The after part is orientated NE–SW and measures 57m long, 16m wide and stands a maximum 3.1m above the seabed. The wreck is thought to be partly buried and/or broken up. There is sediment scouring at the NE end of the vessel. The fore part of the *Bussum* was not identified in the multibeam data during the INSS project.

Printed Sources
Hocking 1989, 110
Wynn 1997, Vol. i, 81

Internet Sources
www.history.navy.mil
www.uboat.net
www.warsailors.com
www.wrecksite.eu

IN HONOUR OF THE
SEAMEN LOST WHILE
SERVING ON IRISH
MERCHANT SHIPS

1939 - 1945

CITY OF LIMERICK 15-7-40
BRENNAN H SULLIVAN J
KERRY HEAD 22-10-40
BEGLEY T BYRNE R DAVIDSON W DRUMMOND G McMAHON M McMAHON   N G NAUGHTON J NICHOLL G
O'REILLY F TOBIN J WILSON J
ARDMORE 11-11-40
BARRY F BOLAND E CRONIN J DESMOND B FENNELL J FLYNN P   ORD T HAAS E JOHNSTON A
KELLEHER J LANE J McGLYNN J McNALLY S MURPHY A G T   O'LEARY T O REGAN J
O'SHEA F POWER JOHN POWER JAMES RAYMOND M RYAN
INNISFALLEN 21-12-40
DOYLE W GEARY D PORTER J RICHARD J
St FINTAN 22-3-41
FRITZSEN K HENDRY N HOWAT J JONES J LEONARD M O'BYRNE D   O'DONNELL M PLUNKETT B
CLONLARA 22-8-41
CARR W GREENE E KAVANACH E LAMBE J McGUIGAN F McKANE   J ROBERTSON A SMITH W
GRANNER J SPENCE R
CITY OF WATERFORD 19-9-41
AFLIN T FURLONG C NAYLOR S MURPHY F KEARNEY E

IRISH PINE 15-11-42
BENT P GASHIN K CLERY P CONNOLLY W CONWAY J CRIGH   WZER F CUSACK F CUSACK T
DALY T DONACH E DOOLEY M DUFFY J FANNING P FLYNN   TT A McCARTHY J MURPHY F
NOLAN J O'BRIEN O O'CALLAGHAN M O'CONNELL J O'CONN   NOGUE T O'NEILL M RYAN S
SHEEHAN P SMITH S TALBOT R TOBIN A TRACY F WAR   D H
KYLECLARE 23-2-43
BARRY E BRANNOCK P BRADY T De BURCA D CRIMES R K   HOPKINS P LARKIN J LYNCH T
MOREAN J MOONEY D O'BRIEN W O'BRIEN R O'BRIEN D O   YAN T SIRMS W TODD U
CYMRIC 23-2-44
BERGIN P BRENNAN J CASSIDY C CROSBIE J FURLONG   B McCONNELL C O'ROURKE W
RYAN M SEAVER P TIERNEY M
LIGHTHOUSE TENDER ISOLDA 19-12-40
DUNNE P FARRELL W HOLLAND W RUSHBY W HAYDE   P
S-TRAWLER LEUKOS 9-3-40
THOMASSON U McLEOD A DONNELLY W SMITH B D   McCARTHY P MULLIGAN T
PILL T CULLEN M HAWKINS J SUMLER R
F-VESSEL NAOMH GARBHAN 2-5-45
CUDDIHY N GRIFFIN J (SEN) GRIFFIN J (JUN)

OTHER DEATHS RECORDED DURING THE
MASTERSON J BRENNAN T CARROLL M CREAN T KEHOE   LARKIN M KENNA J CARROLL J
BYRNE J HALLEY P BURKE L O'NEILL R PAISLEY   E DOOLEY M HENDERSON W BROWN W
ERECTED BY MEMO   TTEE
UNVEILED BY AN t'UACH   NA n'EIREANN
Dr PATRICK
MAY R

COMMITTEE (1977-1991)
AIRMAN PATRICK LAUNDERS (SEAM   OF IRELAND)
ETARY PATRICK SWEENEY (MARITI   TUTE OF IRELAND)
CAPT FRANK FERRIS & CAPT   PE (IRISH ASSOCIATION OF MASTER MARINERS)
EAMUS REDMOND & MICHAEL   (MARINE PORT & GENERAL WORKERS UNION)
GED MEMBERS
WILLIAM STACEY (SEAM   OF IRELAND)
FRANK ELLIS (MARINE PORT   ORKERS UNION)
CAPT H WALSH (IRISH ASSOC   ASTER MARINERS)

Rask (Possible)

GSI ref. code	202
NMS wreck no.	W04190
Location	14km SE of Rosslare harbour, Co. Wexford
Co-ordinates	52 10 8.51N, 006 11 14.86W
Depth of water	77m
Vessel type	Merchant vessel
Vessel dimensions	51m (l), 8m (b), 5m (d)
Date of building	1890
Date of loss	19 October 1941

The identity of this wreck has not yet been confirmed, although available information would appear to indicate that it is that of the *Rask*. It is hoped that further research, survey work and investigations by divers will some day confirm whether this is the case.

Circumstances of loss

The *Rask* was a Norwegian steel steamship of 632 tons, equipped with triple-expansion engines. It was built in 1890 by the Dutch shipbuilders A. A. Wilton van Reede Czn, Papendrecht, and named the *Göteborg*. Initially owned by D/S A/S Marstrand (D. Torm) Copenhagen, the vessel was purchased by Olaus Kvilhaug & Co. A/S, Haugesund, Norway, in 1917 and renamed the *Uno*. It was purchased in 1924 by Sigvart Rasmussen, Haugesund, and renamed the *Rask*, and was eventually acquired by D/S A/S Rask (Sigvald Risanger) in April 1937.

Apart from the everyday risks shipping had to endure while at sea, such as bad weather and rough seas, merchant shipping also had to contend with the threat posed by U-boats, mines and aircraft throughout the battle of the Atlantic. German long-range aircraft, mostly Focke-Wulf Fw200 Condors, bombed and strafed shipping off the Irish coast, as well as acting as spotters for U-boats, earning themselves a reputation as the 'scourge of the Atlantic'. The *Rask* was to suffer such a fate at their hands.

At about 6.30pm on 19 September 1941 the vessel came under attack from three German aircraft near Tuskar Rock, off the coast of Co. Wexford. The *Rask*, with 16 crewmen, was under the command of Captain Sigurd M.J. Martinessen and en route from Cork to Newport, Wales, in ballast. Two of the planes are believed to have been hit during the exchange of fire, with one of them possibly downed by the *Rask*'s five machine guns, which were manned by both crewmen and gunners. The undamaged plane returned and scored a direct hit, causing irreparable damage to the *Rask*, and she sank not long afterwards. The starboard lifeboat left the ship with five men on board and landed at Blackwater, Co. Wexford, the next morning. The port lifeboat, with 12 men on board, unfortunately capsized several times, with seven fatalities brought about by exposure. The remaining crewmen on the lifeboat were rescued at about 6.00am by the British vessel *Wallace Rose*.

On the seafloor

The wreck of the *Rask* measures 57m in length, 12m in width and 9.55m in maximum height, with an average height of 5.4m. The vessel is orientated NE–SW on the seafloor.

Printed Sources
Hocking 1989, 580
Larn & Larn 2002
UKHO Wreck Data 1996
Woodman 2004, 253

Internet Source
www.warsailors.com

Above: The SS *Rask* under way. (Courtesy of the National Maritime Museum, Greenwich)

Above: A 3D, multibeam view of the *Rask* lying upright on the seabed near Tuskar Rock, Co. Wexford.

Opposite: Memorial on City Quay, Dublin, dedicated to seamen who lost their lives while serving on Irish merchant ships during World War II. (Photo Con Brogan)

HMS Curacoa

GSI ref. code	21 and 22
NMS wreck no.	W07242
Location	68km NW of Tory Island, off the coast of Co. Donegal
Co-ordinates	55 50 18.92N, 008 38 07.37W (GSI 21 – bow)
	55 50 06.32 N, 008 38 24.47W (GSI 22 – stern)
Depth of water	122m
Vessel type	Anti-aircraft Cruiser
Vessel dimensions	137m (l), 13m (b), 5m (d)
Date of building	1917
Date of loss	2 October 1942

Circumstances of loss

The *Curacoa* was a light cruiser and one of five Ceres C-class cruisers built between 1916 and 1918. It was built in Pembroke Dock, Wales, in May 1917, weighed 4,290 tons and was capable of 29 knots. It was commissioned on 18 February 1918 and saw service during the final months of World War I. It was refitted as an anti-aircraft cruiser in late 1939 and employed as an escort vessel for transatlantic convoys. It was during one such voyage that the *Curacoa*, under the command of Captain John W. Boutwood, was accidentally lost while escorting the Cunard White Star liner RMS *Queen Mary*. The famous liner was part of a convoy of 27 vessels that was en route from New York to the Clyde and was carrying 15,000 American troops, headed for service with the Allied war effort in Europe. As the convoy was nearing the northern approaches to Ireland, the liner was steaming at 28 knots on an evasive zigzag course when it accidentally collided with the *Curacoa*, striking the cruiser on its port side and splitting the smaller naval vessel in two. The *Curacoa* sank within minutes, with the lost of 338 of the 364 crew on board. The RMS *Queen Mary* received relatively minor damage and continued on her way, without stopping to pick up any survivors from the *Curacoa* for fear of attack from U-boats. It was left

Below: The HMS *Curacoa* was a light cruiser and one of five Ceres C-class cruisers built between 1916 and 1918. (Courtesy of Imperial War Museum)

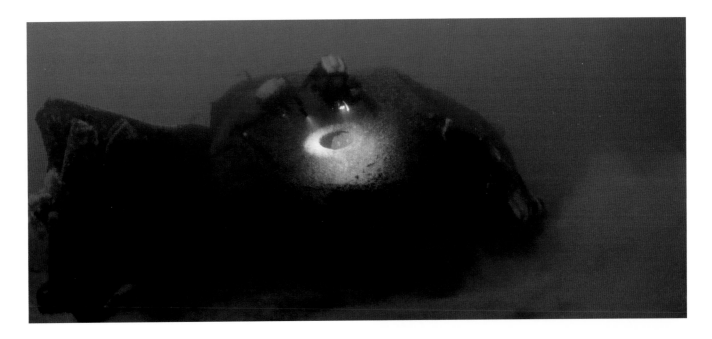

Above: The stern area of the HMS *Curacoa* being investigated by divers 122m below the water surface. (Photo Barry McGill)

to other vessels in the convoy to eventually rescue the remaining 26 survivors, who included the Captain among their number. After the war, an inquiry into the incident assigned two-thirds of the blame to the British Admiralty and the remaining one-third to Cunard White Star for the cause of the incident.

On the seafloor

Today the *Curacoa* sits on the seabed in two parts, nearly 500m apart. The stern section is sitting upright on the seabed and is largely intact, measuring 37m in length, 9m in width, 3.9m in maximum height, with the aft twin 4-inch anti-aircraft gun and single pom pom visible on the deck. The rudder can be just seen under the counter behind tangled netting, centred amidships. The larger bow section is orientated E–W and now lies inverted on the seabed, but along the starboard gunwale there is a gap of about 1m between it and the seabed and much of the crushed superstructure can be made out under the hull. It measures 54m in length, 15m in width and 7.5m in maximum height, with an average height of 3.7m. The Air Defence Position protrudes from under the hull to starboard and an empty compass bowl and the voice pipes that once carried reports of enemy aircraft to the fire control can be seen clearly within. Aft, a single 20mm Oerlikon, which once sat mounted high between the two funnels, sits alongside the torn and jagged hull, which tells us where the *Queen Mary*'s giant bow punched through the cruiser, as if it were made of paper.

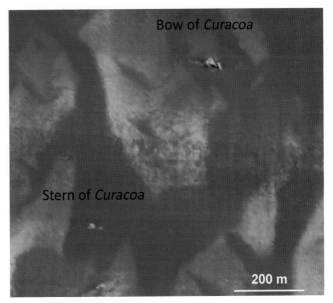

Bow of *Curacoa*

Stern of *Curacoa*

200 m

Above: Multibeam overview of the wreck of the *Curacoa* lying in two parts, almost 500m apart.

Printed Sources

Colledge 2003, 90
Hocking 1989, 172
Larn & Larn 2002

Empire Heritage

Above: The *Empire Heritage* at anchor sometime in early 1943. The newly converted war transport can now be seen equipped with an array of guns, including six Oerlikon anti-aircraft guns, a 12-pounder and a 4-inch gun. (Courtesy of the National Maritime Museum, Greenwich)

GSI ref. code	87
NMS wreck no.	W07306
Location	28km NW of Malin Head, Co. Donegal
Co-ordinates	55 32 33.47N, 007 43 2.21W
Depth of water	65m
Vessel type	Tanker
Vessel dimensions	155m (l), 22m (b), 15m (d)
Date of building	1930
Date of loss	8 September 1944

Circumstances of loss

The *Empire Heritage* was built by Armstrong, Whitworth and Co. in Newcastle-Upon-Tyne for the Kerguelen Sealing & Whaling Co. of Capetown, South Africa. It originally operated as a whaler called the *Tafelberg* and weighed 13,640 tons. After hitting a mine and running ashore in the Bristol Channel in 1941, it was declared a total loss and rebuilt as a tanker for the Ministry of War Transport. The newly renamed *Empire Heritage* weighed 15,702 tons and was capable of 11 knots. It was re-launched in February 1943 and operated by Christian Salvesen & Co., Edinburgh.

The vessel was part of a convoy (HXF-305) of nearly 100 ships, en route from New York to Liverpool and the Clyde, when it was torpedoed and sunk 28km northwest of Malin Head. The tanker was under the command of Captain James Campbell Jamieson and had on board a cargo of military tanks, vehicles, 16,000 tons of fuel, 88 crew and 73 passengers. The submarine that destroyed it, *U-482*, had been patrolling the northwest approaches since 16 August and had already sunk the tanker *Jacksonville*, HMS *Hurst Castle* and SS *Fjordheim* by the time it encountered the *Empire Heritage* and convoy HXF-305. In the early hours of 8 September, *U-482*, under the command of *Kapitänleutnant* Hartmut Graf von Matuschka, fired a number of torpedoes at the convoy, successfully hitting the *Empire Heritage* on its starboard side abaft the bridge. Within ten minutes the tanker had capsized and sunk, with the loss of 113 crew and passengers. The *Pinto*, a convoy rescue ship, was sunk shortly afterwards by the same submarine as it attempted to rescue survivors from the *Empire Heritage*. The survivors of both ships were picked up by HMS *Northern Wave* and landed at Derry.

On the seafloor

In her prime the *Empire Heritage* was an eye-catching ship, but not necessarily the most graceful. Despite this, her wreck is an extraordinary sight. It is orientated NW–SE on the seafloor and covers an area 155m long by 37m wide and has a maximum height of 6.9m. The entire ship has collapsed down and across to starboard, leaving the bulk of the deck and its cargo sitting on the seafloor. Towering over this scene are the 1.5m-girth, 20m-high midships derricks, though these are looking increasingly unstable as the years progress. Scattered around to starboard are the remains of the vessel's cargo that makes this dive unique: the deck cargo of Sherman tanks and 20-ton trucks, seemingly in any position except upright, bar one solitary tank. There is nothing remotely like this extraordinary sight anywhere else in Europe. Aft past the six gigantic Scotch boilers the stern is almost inverted, with a huge propeller dominating the scene and a 4-inch gun lying off to one side.

Above: Diver inspecting the turret of a Sherman tank lying in the vicinity of the *Empire Heritage* wreck. This American-made tank allowed the Allies to successfully confront the German panzer divisions on the Western Front. (Photo Barry McGill)

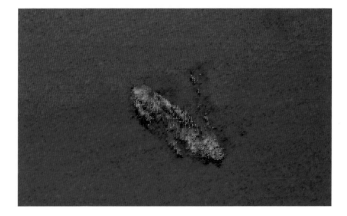

Above: Multibeam view of the wreck and its cargo of tanks and trucks scattered on the seabed. The twisted remains of the wreck show up well in the multibeam imagery.

Printed Sources
Bishop 2002, 50–56
Hocking 1969, 217
Larn & Larn 2002
UKHO Wreck Data
Wynn 1997, Vol. i, 317

Internet Source
www.uboat.net

Following pages: When the *Empire Heritage* sank, its cargo of Sherman tanks, 20-ton trucks and other army provisions spilled out onto the seafloor. Dozens of American-made Sherman tanks now lie scattered, like children's toys, on the seabed around the wreck. (Photo Barry McGill)

Pinto

GSI ref. code	88
NMS wreck no.	W07551
Location	27km NW of Malin Head, Co. Donegal
Co-ordinates	55 32 14.78N, 007 42 57.71W
Depth of water	64m
Vessel type	Convoy Rescue Ship
Vessel dimensions	82.3m (l), 12m (b), 5m (d)
Date of building	1928
Date of loss	8 September 1944

Circumstances of loss

This 1,346-ton vessel from Liverpool was built by Harland and Wolff, Belfast, and owned by MacAndrews & Co., London. The *Pinto* was propelled by 355 horsepower oil engines, capable of attaining 12 knots in speed. On 5 December 1942 the vessel was commissioned as a rescue ship by the Ministry of War Transport. While escorting convoy HXF-305 from Halifax to Liverpool and the Clyde, the *Pinto* (skippered by Captain Lawrence Stanley Boggs) was torpedoed and sunk by *U-482*, commanded by *Kapitänleutnant* Hartmut Graf von Matuschka. At the time the vessel was rescuing the survivors of the *Empire Heritage*, which had been torpedoed and badly damaged by the same U-boat. Accounts of the sinking differ, but between 18 and 21 people on board were lost. Survivors were picked up by HMS *Northern Wave* and landed at Derry. Besides the *Pinto* and *Empire Heritage*, *U-482* also sank three other ships off north Donegal around this time, in late August and early September, namely the tanker *Jacksonville*, HMS *Hurst Castle* and SS *Fjordheim*.

On the seafloor

Only a mile away from the *Empire Heritage* is the bare outline of the *Pinto*. It measures 81m in length, 14m in width and 3.3m in maximum height, with an average height of 0.8m. The vessel is orientated NE–SW on the seafloor and is badly broken up and largely buried. Almost nothing upright remains, except for the huge diesel engine block in the centre of the debris.

Printed Sources
BVLS 1939–1945, 53
Hocking 1989, 554
Larn & Larn 2002
UKHO Wreck Data
Wynn 1997, Vol. i, 317

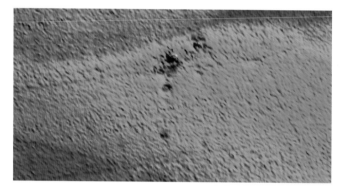

Above: Multibeam view of the wreck of the *Pinto*, which is badly broken up and buried in the seafloor. The most visible part of the wreck is the remains of a diesel engine, which protrude over 3m above the seafloor amongst the scattered debris.

Below: In December 1942 the *Pinto* was armed and commissioned as a convoy rescue ship by the British Ministry of War Transport. It successfully escorted nine convoys until it was torpedoed while rescuing the crew of the *Empire Heritage*. This picture was taken between December 1943 and September 1944. (Courtesy of the National Maritime Museum, Greenwich)

U-743

GSI ref. code	93
NMS wreck no.	W11716
Location	25km NW of Inishtrahull, Co. Donegal
Co-ordinates	55 37 47.96N, 007 25 55.31W
Depth of water	65m
Vessel type	U-boat
Vessel dimensions	67m (l), 6m (b), 5m (d)
Date of building	1942-3
Date of loss	Mid to late September 1944

Circumstances of loss

The submarine *U-743* was one of 577 Type VIIC German submarines commissioned and one of the most commonly built U-boats during World War II. It weighed 761 tons on the surface, measured 67m long and could carry a crew of up to 44 men. It was capable of 17 knots on the surface, powered by 2,800–3,200 horsepower engines, and had a range of 6,500 nautical miles if travelling on the surface at 12 knots. It could reach a maximum depth of 200m and could carry both mines and torpedoes. It was built by Schichau of Danzig, launched in March 1943 and was commissioned into service in May of the same year. It initially carried out equipment tests in the Baltic Sea in August 1943 before entering full service. It was commanded by *Oberleutnant zur See* Helmut Kandzior and carried out two patrols during its service, but neither sank nor damaged any vessel during its war career. The first patrol was off

Norway, from June to August 1944, where it unsuccessfully engaged a Liberator aircraft of the 86th Squadron. The submarine's second patrol was to the west of the Hebrides, in August 1944, where it is now known to have been lost off the north coast of Donegal some time in the last days of September. The exact cause of loss is unknown, but all 50 crew on board were presumed dead. In July 2001 the wreck of *U-743* was identified by divers of the Operation Deadlight Expedition, led by Innes McCartney.

On the seafloor

The wreck of the *U-743* measures 58m in length, 7.5m in width and 4.7m in maximum height, with an average height of 2.1m. The submarine is orientated NE–SW on the seafloor. In contrast to most of the other U-boat wrecks in the area, this Type VII was a war loss. The wreck is essentially intact, but the attack periscope has been bent right over, with the lens buried in the seabed, and the *schnorchel* has been broken off at the height of the conning tower, with its base still upright and located in its collar on the conning tower. The fact that all hatches on the wreck are closed would suggest that it was schorcheling when it was sunk, possibly due to a collision with an unknown vessel.

Printed Sources
Miller 2000, 27
Möller & Brack 2004, 73
Rossler 1981, 54-5
Wynn 1997, Vol. ii, 145

Internet Source
www.periscopepublishing.com

Above: The *U-743* at Gdansk (formerly Danzig), docked along the quayside on 15 May 1943. The U-boat is photographed adorned with laurel garlands (a symbol of victory) and flags to celebrate its commission into service. (Courtesy of the Deutsches U-Boot Museum)

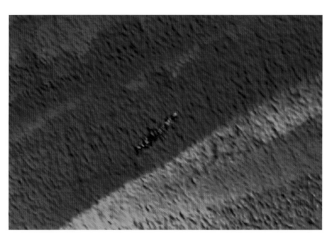

Above: The long slender shape of the U-boat is clearly visible in the multibeam imagery.

U-281

GSI ref. code	76
NMS wreck no.	W10131
Location	30km NW of Malin Head, Co. Donegal
Co-ordinates	55 35 28.07N, 007 41 28.18W
Depth of water	67m
Vessel type	U-boat
Vessel dimensions	67m (l), 6m (b), 5m (d)
Date of building	January 1943
Date of loss	30 November 1945

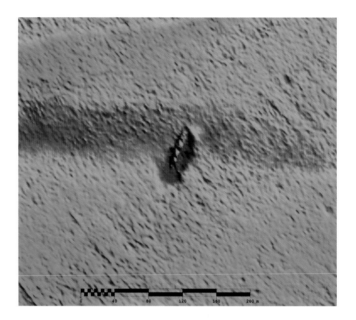

Above: Multibeam overview of the remains of the *U-281* on the seabed at a depth of 67m. A large scour has developed along the E side of the U-boat.

Below: The *U-281* docked alongside several other Type VIIC U-boats. (Courtesy of the Deutsches U-Boot Museum)

Circumstances of loss

U-281 was one of 577 Type VIIC German submarines commissioned and one of the most commonly built U-boats during World War II. It weighed 761 tons surfaced, measured 67m long and could carry a crew of up to 44 men. It was capable of 17 knots on the surface, had 2,800–3,200 horsepower engines and a range of 6,500 miles if travelling on the surface at 12 knots. The Type VIIC U-boat could reach a maximum depth of 200m and could carry both mines and torpedoes.

Above: The *U-281* being prepared to be towed out to sea for disposal during Operation Deadlight. (Courtesy of the Deutsches U-Boot Museum)

It was built at Bremer Vulkan in Vegesack, Germany, and was commissioned into service on 27 February 1943, under the command of *Kapitänleutnant* Heinz von Davidson. *U-281* carried out four patrols during its service and was involved in a number of engagements in the North Atlantic. During one such engagement, in October 1943, it shot down a Royal Canadian Air Force Sunderland southwest of Iceland. Three crew of *U-281* were wounded during this encounter. The submarine spent much of 1944 patrolling off Britain and Ireland, but failed to sink any vessels. At the end of hostilities *U-281* surrendered at Kristiansand, Norway, in May 1945 and was brought to Loch Ryan in Scotland. The submarine was due to be scuttled as part of Operation Deadlight and the Polish destroyer *Blyskawica* towed it out into open water. It never reached its destination, however, as 30km northwest of Malin Head it sank. It now lies in 67m of water.

On the seafloor

In 2001 the wreck was identified by divers during the Operation Deadlight Expedition, led by Innes McCartney. It measures 41m in length, 7m in width and 3.1m in maximum height, with an average height of 0.7m. The submarine is orientated NNE–SSW on the seafloor, is in poor condition and lies on its port side. The bow tubes have been dragged off to one side, with all four still held together in the bow bracket, and now the forward end of the pressure hull marks the beginning of the main wreck. A *schnorchel* with anti-radar covering and air radar warning dipole is folded on the deck. The conning tower hatch is shut, while the bow torpedo loading hatch is open, allowing the interior of the torpedo room to be inspected.

Printed Sources

Miller 2000, 27
Möller & Brack 2004, 73
Rossler 1981, 54–5
Wynn 1997, Vol. i, 197–8

Internet Source

www.periscopepublishing.com

U-218

GSI ref. code	117
NMS wreck no.	W10125
Location	13km NNW of Malin Head, Co. Donegal
Co-ordinates	55 29 58.45N, 007 25 56.82W
Depth of water	57m
Vessel type	U-boat
Vessel dimensions	77m (l), 6m (b), 5m (d)
Date of building	1941
Date of loss	4 December 1945

Circumstances of loss

U-218 was one of six Type VIID German submarines commissioned and the only one of its type to survive the war. It weighed 965 tons surfaced, measured 77m long and could carry a crew of up to 44 men. It was capable of 16 knots on the surface, had 2,800–3,200 horsepower engines and a range of 8,100 nautical miles if travelling on the surface at 12 knots. It could reach a maximum depth of 200m and could carry up to 15 mines and 14 torpedoes. It was built by F.G. Krupp Germania Werft AG in Kiel, launched in December 1941 and commissioned into service in January 1942. Commanders of the vessel at different stages in its career were *Kapitänleutnant* Richard Becker and *Kapitänleutnant* Rupprecht Stock.

U-218 spent most of its service operating in the Atlantic and had a number of lucky escapes, sustaining serious

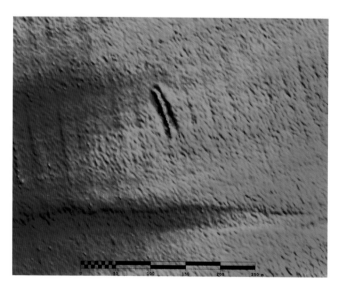

Above: The characteristic long, narrow shape of a submarine is clearly visible in the multibeam image of the *U-218*. The U-boat is in good condition on the seafloor, but lists to its port side at a 45-degree angle.

damage on several occasions. In October 1942, U-218 was ordered to Gibraltar to attack the Allied Forces invading North Africa, but the submarine was forced to return to its naval base at Brest after being damaged by depth charges from HMS *Wrestler*. On 2 August 1943 U-218 narrowly escaped destruction after it was attacked while searching in the Bay of Biscay for survivors from the destroyed U-383. A Wellington aircraft from Squadron 547/B attacked the U-boat, causing some damage and injuring six crew. Depth charges dropped by the Wellington failed to sink U-218, but did force it to return to base for repairs. The submarine had a small number of successes, damaging a convoy ship with torpedoes in August 1942. In September 1943, after laying 12 mines in the Caribbean, U-218 sank a sailing freighter off Trinidad. In 1944 U-218 laid mines in the English Channel, causing damage to SS *Empire Halberd* and sinking a 352-ton minesweeper trawler, the *Kurd*. In April 1945 one of its mines sank the fishing trawler *Ethel Crawford* west of Ailsa Craig, while it was operating off Scotland. By the time the war had ended, U-218 had sunk three ships and damaged two others. It surrendered at Bergen, Norway, on 8 May 1945. From there it was transferred to Loch Ryan in Scotland, to be scuttled as part of Operation Deadlight. On 4 December 1945, while being towed out by HMS *Southdown*, it sank 13km NNW of Malin Head.

On the seafloor

The wreck of U-218 was identified by divers during the Operation Deadlight Expedition in 2001. The wreck sits on the seabed, with a 45-degree list to port. Apart from minor damage to the bow and stern, and the loss of the conning tower cladding, it is completely intact. The five-chute mine section behind the conning tower is reminiscent of a modern ballistic missile submarine and the huge chutes, running all the way through the depth of the hull, are easily big enough for a diver to swim through. The wreck measures 65m in length, 7m in width and 3.9m in maximum height, with an average height of 2.2m. The submarine is orientated NNW–SSE on the seafloor. Sediment scouring has occurred around the vessel.

Printed Sources
Miller 2000, 27
Möller & Brack 2004, 94
Rossler 1981, 54-5
Wynn 1997, Vol. i, 159-61

Internet Source
www.periscopepublishing.com

Top: The *U-218* underway in its dazzle camouflage. (Courtesy of the Deutsches U-Boot Museum)

Bottom: Underwater image of the *U-218* listing on its port side. Its outer hull is slowly decaying, exposing its inner workings. The conning tower is visible in the background, with one of its five mine shafts visible to the fore. (Photo Barry McGill)

U-778

GSI ref. code	100
NMS wreck no.	W10144
Location	18km NW of Malin Head, Co. Donegal
Co-ordinates	55 32 29.04N, 007 28 46.34W
Depth of water	67m
Vessel type	U-boat
Vessel dimensions	67m (l), 6m (b), 5m (d)
Date of building	1942–4
Date of loss	4 December 1945

Circumstances of loss

U-778 was one of 577 Type VIIC German submarines commissioned and one of the most commonly built U-boats during World War II. It weighed 761 tons surfaced, measured 67m long and could carry a crew of up to 44 men. It was capable of 17 knots on the surface, had 2,800–3,200 horsepower engines and a range of 6,500 nautical miles if travelling on the surface at 12 knots. It could reach a maximum depth of 200m and carried both mines and torpedoes. It was built by Kriegsmarine-Werft, Wilhelmshaven, was launched in May 1944 and commissioned into service on 7 July 1944. The submarine carried out one patrol off the Scottish coast under the command of *Kapitänleutnant* Ralf Jürs, but failed to sink any ships. It was surrendered at Bergen, in Norway, in May

Above: The crew of the *U-778* celebrate the commissioning of the Type VIIC submarine into service on 7 July 1944 at the Kreigsmarine shipyard in Wilhelmshaven. (Courtesy of the Deutsches U-Boot Museum)

1945. It was transferred to Loch Ryan, Scotland, where it was to be scuttled along with 115 other U-boats off the northwest coast of Ireland as part of Operation Deadlight. However, *U-778* accidentally sank while under tow to the dump site on 4 December 1945, approximately 18km northwest of Malin Head.

On the seafloor

The wreck of *U-778* was identified by divers during the Operation Deadlight Expedition in 2001. The *U-778* is one of the most intact U-boats that can be dived in Irish waters. It measures 54m in length, 5m in width and 4m in maximum height, with an average height of 2.4m. The U-boat is orientated NW–SE on the seafloor, with the distinctive long, narrow shape of a submarine visible on the multibeam sonar. Unusually, the conning tower retains its cladding and the bow is undamaged. The *schnorchel* can be found folded down on the deck.

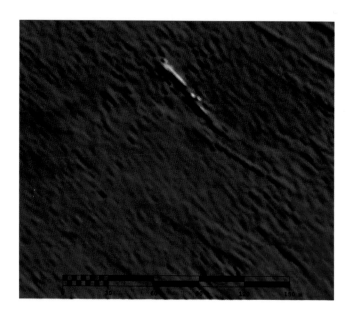

Above: The distinctive long, narrow shape of a submarine is clearly visible in the multibeam image of the *U-778*.

Printed Sources
Miller 2000, 27
Möller & Brack 2004, 73
Rossler 1981, 54–5
Wynn 1997, Vol. ii, 162

Internet Source
www.periscopepublishing.com

U-149

GSI ref. code	62
NMS wreck no.	W10121
Location	43km NE of Tory Island, off the coast of Co. Donegal
Co-ordinates	55 38 33.94N, 008 0 36.47W
Depth of water	83m
Vessel type	U-boat
Vessel dimensions	44m (l), 5m (b), 3.9m (d)
Date of building	1940
Date of loss	21 December 1945

Circumstances of loss

U-149 was one of 16 Type IID German submarines commissioned during the war. It weighed 314 tons surfaced, measured 44m long and could carry a crew of 25 men. It was capable of 12.7 knots on the surface, propelled by 700 horsepower engines, and had a range of 3,200 miles if travelling on the surface. The Type IID submarine could reach a maximum depth of 100m and carried six torpedoes. It was built by Deutsche Werke in Kiel, launched in 1940 and became operational in 1941. It does not appear to have seen much action during World War II, spending much of the time as a training boat, although it did sink a Soviet submarine (*M-99*) while on patrol at the entrance to the Gulf of Finland. It surrendered at the end of the war, in early May 1945, and was brought to Loch Ryan from Wilhelmshaven for disposal as part of Operation Deadlight. While being towed to the disposal site, the towline for *U-149* parted in bad weather and the U-boat was sunk by gunfire instead.

Below: Photographed after hostilities had ceased, the crew of the *U-149* stand to attention for the last time while departing Wilhelmshaven, Germany, for Loch Ryan in Scotland on 30 June 1945 for disposal as part of Operation Deadlight. (Courtesy of the Deutsches U-Boot Museum)

Above: Senior officers catch some sun and fresh air on the deck of the *U-149*. (Courtesy of the Deutsches U-Boot Museum)

On the seafloor

The wreck of *U-149* measures 20m in length, 4.5m in width and 3.3m in maximum height, with an average height of 0.6m. The submarine is orientated NW–SE on the seafloor. Sediment scouring has occurred around the vessel.

Printed Sources

Miller 2000, 22
Möller & Brack 2004, 68

Rossler 1981, 54–5
Wynn 1997, Vol. i, 116

U-155

GSI ref. code	91
NMS wreck no.	W10122
Location	24km NW of Malin Head, Co. Donegal
Co-ordinates	55 34 17N, 007 34 40.58W
Depth of water	70m
Vessel type	U-boat
Vessel dimensions	77m (l), 7m (b), 5m (b)
Date of building	1940–41
Date of loss	21 December 1945

Circumstances of loss

U-155 was one of 54 Type IXC German submarines commissioned. It weighed 1,120 tons surfaced, measured 76m long and could carry a crew of 48 men. It was capable of 18.3 knots surfaced, had 4,400 horsepower engines and a range of 11,400 miles if travelling on the surface at 12 knots. The Type IXC U-boat could reach a maximum depth of 230m and carried up to 22 torpedoes. It was

Above: The Type IXC U-boat photographed while on patrol. The German submarine sunk 26 ships during its four-year war career. (Courtesy of the Deutsches U-Boot Museum)

built by A.G. Weser of Bremen, launched on 12 May 1941 and commissioned into service on 23 August 1941. In the submarine's four-year career it was responsible for sinking 26 ships: 20 of these were destroyed while operating in the western Atlantic, and a further three ships were targeted off Portugal and Morocco during 1942. *U-155* survived the war and surrendered in May 1945 at Wilhelmshaven. It was transferred to Loch Ryan, Scotland, on 21 June 1945 and was designated to be scuttled, along with 115 other U-boats, off the northwest coast of Ireland as part of Operation Deadlight. The submarine failed to reach the designated site and was sunk on 21 December 1945, 25km northwest of Malin Head.

Opposite, Top: The *U-155* sits upright on the seabed at a depth of 70m. The disintegrating remains of the stern are covered in sea anemones. (Photo Raymond Mijdam (raymond@cyber-gate.nl))

Opposite, Bottom: Diver investigates the disintegrating conning tower of the *U-155*. (Photo Raymond Mijdam (raymond@cyber-gate.nl))

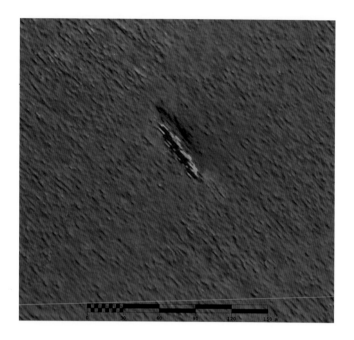

On the seafloor

In 2001 the wreck was identified by divers during the Operation Deadlight Expedition, led by Innes McCartney. The wreck of the *U-155* measures 52m in length, 5.5m in width and 4.3m in maximum height, with an average height of 3.9m. The wreck lies upright and is orientated NW–SE on the seafloor. Scouring has occurred along the northeast side of the vessel. This Type IXC U-boat sits upright on the seabed. The forward hydroplanes and torpedo tubes have fallen off to one side, revealing the front of the pressure hull. The outer cladding hull is in good condition and the 'beamy' shape of the Type IXC is very evident. The *schnorchel* can be found on the starboard side of the foredeck and the reinforcing for the 'wintergarden' anti-aircraft position is also visible. The conning tower hatch is open and as the lower hatch is also open, the interior of the control room can be seen.

Above: The characteristic long, narrow shape of a U-boat is evident in the multibeam imagery.

Below: The outer hull of the bow section of the *U-155* has totally disintegrated, revealing the forward torpedo tubes. (Photo Raymond Mijdam (raymond@cyber-gate.nl))

Printed Sources
Miller 2000, 37
Möller & Brack 2004, 98
Rossler 1981, 54–5
Wynn 1997, Vol. i, 119–20

Internet Sources
www.periscopepublishing.com
www.uboat.net

U-1009

GSI ref. code	171
NMS wreck no.	W10114
Location	29km WNW of Tory Island, off the coast of Co. Donegal
Co-ordinates	55 31 29.53N, 007 23 57.91W
Depth of water	55m
Vessel type	U-boat
Vessel dimensions	67m (l), 6m (b), 4.9m (d)
Date of building	1943-4
Date of loss	5 January 1946

Printed Sources
Miller 2000, 27
Möller & Brack 2004, 73
Rossler 1981, 54–5
Wynn 1997, Vol. ii, 215–16

Internet Source
www.periscopepublishing.com

Circumstances of loss

The *U-1009* was one of 88 Type VII C/41 U-boats commissioned. It weighed 759 tons surfaced, measured 67m long and could carry a crew of up to 44 men. It was capable of 17 knots on the surface, had 2,800–3,200 horse-power engines and a range of 6,500 miles if travelling on the surface at 12 knots. It could reach a maximum depth of 250m and carried up to 39 mines and 14 torpedoes. It was built by Blohm & Voss, Hamburg, launched in January 1944 and commissioned into service on 10 February 1944. This submarine was under the command of *Oberleutnant zur See* Klaus Hilgendorf for most of its service. It operated in British waters in January 1945 and was involved in an engagement with a patrol boat and a destroyer, but failed to sink either. It was also involved in weather-reporting duties during this period. No vessels were sunk or damaged by this U-boat. *U-1009* survived the war intact and surrendered itself in Loch Eriboll, Scotland, on 10 May 1945, where it was designated to be scuttled, along with 115 other surrendered U-boats, off the northwest coast of Ireland as part of Operation Deadlight. On 5 January 1946 the submarine was deliberately sunk using gunfire after its tow cable broke 29km north of Tory Island.

On the seafloor

The wreck of *U-1009* measures 46m in length, 6m in width and 1.7m in maximum height, with an average height of 1m. The submarine is orientated N–S on the seafloor. The multibeam sonar image shows the wreck to be partly buried and/or broken up. The conning tower and the forward end of the pressure hull are peppered with shell-holes. The majority of the superstructure has come away, as have the bow tubes, and the top section of the *schnorchel* now lies on the seabed.

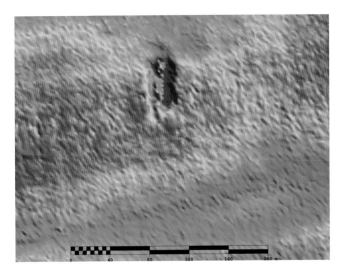

Above: The multibeam imagery shows the damaged remains of the *U-1009* on the seabed at a depth of 55m.

Above: *U-1009* arriving into Lisahally, outside Derry. The 19th-century fort at Culmore Point, now housing the Lough Foyle Yacht Club, can be seen in the background. (Courtesy of the Royal Navy Submarine Museum)

Following pages: *U-1009* surrendering to the Royal Navy in May 1945 and flying the obligatory black flag, as was required under the terms of surrender. (Courtesy of the Imperial War Museum)

U-2506

GSI ref. code	101
NMS wreck no.	W10127
Location	26km NW of Malin Head, Co. Donegal
Co-ordinates	55 30 59.69N, 007 30 25.45W
Depth of water	67m
Vessel type	Submarine
Vessel dimensions	77m (l), 7m (b), 6m (d)
Date of building	1944
Date of loss	5 January 1946

Circumstances of loss

The *U-2506* was a Type XXI German submarine, a new high-speed 'electro boat', weighing 1,621 tons and capable of 15.6–17.6 knots. It had two 2,200 horsepower engines and a range of 11,150 nautical miles if travelling on the surface at 12 knots. It could reach a maximum depth of around 280m and carried up to 23 torpedoes, or alternatively 14 torpedoes and 12 mines, and was manned by a crew of 57 men. It was built by Blohm & Voss, Hamburg, launched in August 1944 and commissioned into service in the same month. This submarine was under the command of *Kapitänleutnant* Horst von Schroeter (August 1944–May 1945), who earlier in the war had sunk seven vessels, most notably an enemy submarine, the HMS *P-615*, off the coast of Sierra Leone in April 1943. The *U-2506* departed Germany for Bergen, Norway, during the last days of the war, but never carried out war patrols. This submarine was faster than any previous U-boat and possessed an integral *Schnorchel*, which allowed it to stay submerged as long as food and fuel allowed. Clearly representing a significant development in submarine design and technology, the Type XXI submarine had much better facilities for its crew, was quieter and could remain underwater for the greater part of a mission. On 14 June 1945, as part of Operation Deadlight, *U-2506* was transferred to Lisahally, Northern Ireland, and was sunk on 5 January 1946.

On the seafloor

The wreck of *U-2506* measures 62m in length, 5m in width and 6.2m in maximum height, with an average height of 3.4m. The submarine is orientated ENE–WSW on the

Above: Multibeam imagery of *U-2506*, one of the most intact U-boats lying off the Irish coast.

Opposite: The *U-2506* was a Type XXI German submarine, a new high speed 'electro boat'. It is pictured here moored alongside the *U-930* at Kristiansand, Norway, at the end of April 1945, just days before the war ended. It subsequently departed for Bergen, Norway, but never carried out war patrols. (Courtesy of the Deutsches U-Boot Museum)

seafloor. In contrast to the extensively damaged *U-2511*, this Type XXI is essentially undamaged and is a truly magnificent sight for submarine afficionados. When first discovered, the conning tower together with the fore and aft flak positions were completely intact, but now the flak positions have either fallen or are in the process of falling off onto the seabed and a lot of the external cladding is missing. The 20mm gun barrels on both turrets are still in place, however. The only other real damage apparent is that the rudder has fallen off. Forward, the Balkongerat hydrophone array, a further development of that found on the *U-1271*, is clearly visible.

Printed Sources
Bishop 2006, 109
Miller 2000, 60
Möller & Brack 2004, 110
Wynn 1997, Vol. ii, 256

Internet Sources
www.periscopepublishing.com
www.uboat.net

U-2511

GSI ref. code	85
NMS wreck no.	W10209
Location	26km NW of Malin Head, Co. Donegal
Co-ordinates	55 34 45.19N, 007 37 33.85W
Depth of water	66m
Vessel type	U-boat
Vessel dimensions	77m (l), 7m (b), 6m (d)
Date of building	1944
Date of loss	7 January 1946

Circumstances of loss

U-2511 was the first Type XXI German submarine to make an operational patrol in the last days of the war. This vessel represented a new high-speed 'electro boat', weighing 1,621 tons and carrying a crew of 57. It was not only faster underwater and quieter than other U-boats, it could also outrun many naval escorts while still submerged. The Type XXI possessed an integral *Schnorchel*, which allowed it to stay underwater as long as food and fuel were available, making its detection very difficult for the Allies. However, most submarines of this type failed to emerge from training or from shipyards, with only this single example attaining operational status before the war ended. Its torpedo tubes were fitted with a hydraulic loading system, which allowed for a complete

reloading in about 20 minutes, rather than the several hours it took for other U-boats. This new submarine type was capable of 15.6–17.6 knots, had two 2,200 horsepower engines and a range of 11,150 nautical miles if travelling on the surface at 12 knots. It could reach a maximum depth of around 280m and carried up to 23 torpedoes, or alternatively 14 torpedoes and 12 mines. It was built by Blohm & Voss, Hamburg, launched in September 1944 and commissioned into service in the same month.

The innovative *U-2511* was under the command of *Korvettenkapitän* Adalbert Schnee (September 1944–May 1945), a U-boat ace who had previously sunk 23 ships, including the *Nils Gorthon*, which was lost off Malin Head. The *U-2511* departed Germany in mid-March 1945 for Norway, to carry out deep-water trials in the Oslo-Fjord. On 30 April it set out from Bergen on its first mission, intending to patrol the Caribbean, but the ceasefire was called en route, just one day into its journey. A few hours later, on the return trip to Norway, the submarine encountered a British naval group, including the cruiser HMS *Norfolk*. The U-boat approached to within 500m of the British warship without any sonar contact from the enemy destroyer. Schnee had the opportunity to make

Below: The *U-2511*, painted white, moored alongside the *U-2506* (*left*) and the *U-3514* (*right*) at Bergen at the end of the war. (Courtesy of the Deutsches U-Boot Museum)

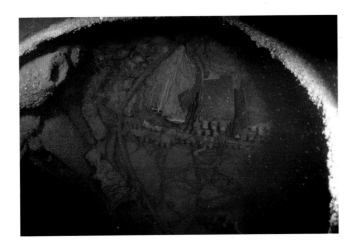

Above: The inner workings of the U-boat are visible through the decaying hull, revealing an array of batteries. (Photo Raymond Mijdam (raymond@cyber-gate.nl))

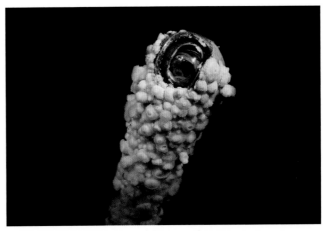

Above: Marine growth has encrusted the periscope, though its lens is still fully intact. (Photo Raymond Mijdam (raymond@cyber-gate.nl))

an absolutely deadly attack against the cruiser, but as a ceasefire had been called he desisted from doing so. Instead, he returned the submarine to Bergen and surrendered it on 9 May. On 14 June, as part of Operation Deadlight, *U-2511* was transferred to Lisahally in Northern Ireland. It was subsequently sunk using gunfire after its tow cable broke on 7 January 1946, 26km NW of Malin Head.

On the seafloor

In 2001 the wreck site was identified by divers during the Operation Deadlight Expedition, led by Innes McCartney. The *U-2511* lies on its port side and is relatively intact, measuring 65m in length, 10m in width and 5.6m in maximum height, with an average height of 2.4m. It is orientated N–S on the seafloor and shows sediment scouring on her east side. The stem is missing and all six of the torpedo tubes can be seen. Aft, the massive conning tower rises up over the wreck. While the forward flak turret was still in place when the wreck was first discovered, it has now joined the aft turret on the seabed. The sky periscope is slightly extended and the optics are visible. Aft of the conning tower the wreck is essentially intact all the way to the stern, where the aft hydroplanes and a single rudder can be seen. As the *U-2511* was sunk by gunfire, shell damage is visible in many areas. One of the biggest holes is in her starboard side, alongside the conning tower, and a mass of cabling and batteries is visible along the keel section of the wreck.

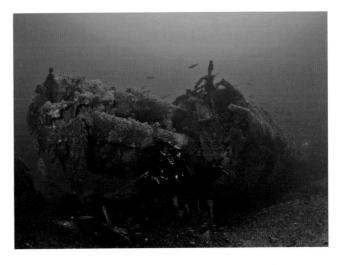

Above: The outer hull of the bow section of the *U-2511* has totally disintegrated, revealing the forward torpedo tubes. A diver investigates the tubes from below. (Photo Raymond Mijdam (raymond@cyber-gate.nl))

Printed Sources
Bishop 2006, 109
Mallmann Showell 2006, 104
Miller 2000, 60
Möller & Brack 2004, 110
Wynn 1997, Vol. ii. 256–7

Internet Source
www.periscopepublishing.com
www.uboat.net

Following pages: *U-2511* lies on its port side and is largely intact, although its conning tower is now devoid of external cladding. (Photo Rich Stevenson of Diving and Marine Solutions)

6 Post-war Shipwrecks

Karl Brady and Fionnbarr Moore

Merchant navies throughout the world suffered heavy losses during World War II and by the end of the conflict nearly 3,000 Allied merchant ships had been sunk. However, global trade increased rapidly in the decades following the war, which resulted in faster and better-built ships being developed and brought into service. Just as steam-powered engines had replaced the sail as a method of propulsion in the 19th and early 20th centuries, from the 1920s on oil-powered vessels continued to replace coal-powered steam vessels.

By the 1950s diesel-powered ships had almost totally replaced all steam-powered vessels in the fishing and merchant fleets around Ireland and Europe, and this reliance on oil still remains largely the case to this day. Ships also increased in size, with the advent of vessels such as the super-tankers. Older cargo ships became less viable and therefore less numerous as the bulk carrier and giant container ships could now carry far greater quantities of cargo. Advances in ship technology and design, such as containerisation, combined with safer navigational aids, including radar, gyroscopic compass, improved radio communication and detailed navigational charts, resulted in much safer travel at sea and lower incidences of wrecks occurring off the Irish coast. Nonetheless, the loss of the MV *Bolivar* (see p.172), which ran aground on the treacherous sands of the Kish Bank during a snow storm in March 1947, during the infamous cold spell of that year, served as a stark reminder of the dangers of venturing out to sea, even in the most advanced vessels of their time.

There were other notable tragedies in this period: in January 1979, an oil tanker, the *Betelgeuse*, exploded while berthed at an oil terminal on Whiddy Island in Bantry Bay, with the loss of fifty lives. The seabed-clearance operations in the wake of the *Betelgeuse* disaster, which were carried out in 1981, led to the discovery of the wreck of *La Surveillante* (see p.28). In 1988 the bulk ore carrier, the *Kowloon Bridge*, went aground on rocks off Toe Head, near Baltimore, Co. Cork. The loss of oil, both as fuel and

cargo, from these large vessels resulted in serious pollution of the surrounding coastal areas. In November 1991 the *Kilkenny*, a container ship, collided with another vessel in Dublin Bay, with the loss of three lives.

The waters around Ireland continued to be seen as a resource that could be used to boost the economy. Bord Iascaigh Mhara (BIM, the Fisheries Board) was established in 1962 to aid the development of the fishing industry, which continued to see significant growth in the amount of fish being landed and exported from the 1950s onwards. Although membership of the EEC in 1972 brought benefits to the country's economy, the opening up of Irish waters to other Member States, combined with the introduction of fishing quota systems and the restriction of Irish fishing boats to only 4% of the European annual catch, all worked against fishing interests in Ireland. Today, fishing fleets as a whole throughout Europe have to contend with stringent quota systems, greater competition from the Far East and South America, along with declining fish stocks. The dangers for fishing boats working at sea have not gone away and fishing boats continue to be lost in the seas around Ireland, all too often with the tragic loss of life.

Cruise liners have recently provided a boost for Irish tourism, with over 200 cruisers calling into Irish ports each year, carrying around half a million passengers and crew. Recreational use of the sea has also seen exponential growth since the end of World War II, with numerous sailing, diving, surfing, canoeing and windsurfing clubs established around the coast. This has placed a strain on the already stretched lifeboat and coastguard services, whose members continue to put their lives at risk in order to save others. For example, the RNLI has reportedly saved over 139,000 lives around Britain and Ireland since its inception in 1824, including some of the crew and passengers of the MV *Bolivar*.

In 1946 the Naval Service replaced the Marine and Coastwatching Service, which had been established in 1939 to maintain a watch on Ireland's coastal waters during the war. For a very brief period the *Muirchú*, which had already served as a fisheries patrol vessel and had seen service through the 1916 Rising and both world wars, became the first ship to be commissioned into the Naval Service. However, the *Muirchú*'s long years of service had taken a toll on the ship and in 1946–7 it was replaced by three ex-Royal Navy corvettes. Those replacement vessels continued in operation until 1970. Since then, the Irish Naval Service has continued to expand and is now recognised as a modern and effective naval service, comparable in this regard to any service in the world. Its fleet comprises eight patrol ships, which are responsible for the defence of Ireland's territorial waters, maritime surveillance and fisheries protection. Sadly, however, Irish Shipping Ltd, which was set up to secure vital wartime supplies in 1941, went into liquidation in 1984 after providing an invaluable service to the Irish state for more than four decades.

In the period since World War II, the story of Ireland's coastal waters has changed considerably, thanks to new technologies, policies and priorities. While the fishing industry has undoubtedly suffered in the changes wrought over the last thirty years, there is now a faint beacon of hope on the horizon thanks to recent changes in the quotas allowed to Irish fishermen together with better management of fish stocks. It is hoped that these measures will protect and enhance this important industry and its long-term sustainability. The Naval Service has adapted with the changing times and serves the country well. One part of the story remains unchanged, however: the power of the sea to take boats. Although there are fewer wrecks to account for in this period, there is still tragic loss of vessels and lives.

THE IRISH TIMES, THURSDAY, MARCH 6,

BROKEN VESSEL SEEN FROM AIR

A picture taken of part of the Bolivar, which broke in two on the Kish sandbank, as our photographer's plane flew between the two parts of the ship at a height of 40 feet.

SIR STAFFORD CRIPPS CONVINCED THAT

Above: The stern end of the MV *Bolivar*, photographed from the air a day after the vessel went aground on the Kish Bank, in March 1947. (Courtesy of *The Irish Times*)

MV Bolivar

Compiled by Cormac Lowth

GSI ref. code	283
NMS wreck no.	W09480
Location	Kish Bank, off the coast of Co. Dublin
Co-ordinates	53 16 03.44N, 05 55 32.53W
Depth of water	9m
Vessel type	Cargo vessel
Vessel dimensions	137m (l), 17.5m (b), 7.5m (d)
Date of building	1946
Date of loss	4 March 1947

Above: The wreck of the *Bolivar* broken in two amidships, as photographed from the air a day after the vessel went aground. (Courtesy of *The Irish Times*)

Circumstances of loss

The MV *Bolivar* was a 5,320-ton cargo vessel and at the time of its loss was owned by the Norwegian shipping company, Fred Olsen. The cargo ship was laid down in the yard of Akers Mekaniske Verksted of Oslo in 1939 and was launched, ready for fitting out, in 1940. However, following the German invasion of Norway in April of 1940, the ship lay alongside the quay wall at the Akers yard for the duration of the war. The *Bolivar* was finally completed in 1946, setting out on her maiden voyage, to South America, in December of that year. It was upon her return from Buenos Aires to Dublin via Liverpool in early March 1947, with a cargo of grain and bales of leather, that the diesel-powered vessel ran aground on the Kish Bank during a snow storm.

Several attempts were made to take the vessel off the bank, but the wind direction and the falling tide both

conspired to keep her stuck fast. As the tide continued to drop, the ship broke in two amidships, with the fore part of the vessel drifting clear and settling 100m away from the stern section. A Dublin-based tug, the *Coliemore*, and a Dún Laoghaire lifeboat, the *Dun Leary 2*, came to the *Bolivar*'s aid and successfully rescued the 39 crew and 12 passengers. Despite hopes of salvaging the stern section, both the ship and cargo became a total loss. The bow section remained largely intact and sank, while the after section was cut down to about the main deck line and was partially salvaged by the Hammond Lane Scrap Company in 1948.

On the seafloor

At the time of its loss the wreck was largely dispersed because she was an obstruction to navigation, but nonetheless a substantial amount of the ship's hull and machinery remain to be seen. The bow section initially remained largely intact and sank beneath the surface, while the after section was cut down to about the main deck line. Today the wreck lies in two main parts, with the stern measuring 83m in length, 16m in width and 5.34m in maximum height. The stern is orientated E–W on the seabed, in a general sea depth of 10m. The remains of the fore section of the vessel lie over 100m to the NE and are largely buried.

Below: Multibeam view of the 83m long aft-end of the wreck. The remains of the two seven-cylinder diesel engines form the highest part of the wreck, as illustrated by the red colours in the multibeam imagery. Also note the large sand wave to the right (S) of the wreck, which is threatening to cover over the wreck.

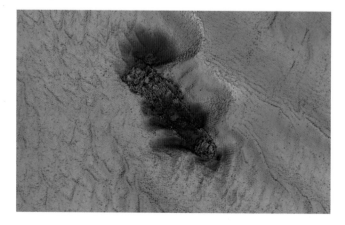

Printed Sources

Lowth 2002, 50–63
The Irish Times, 5 March 1947;
6 March 1947; 7 March 1947;
8 March 1947

Internet Sources

www.mii.connect.ie

Muirchú

GSI ref. code	272
NMS wreck no.	W04039
Location	5.1km SW of the Saltee Islands, off the coast of Co. Wexford
Co-ordinates	52 04 08.40N, 006 35 06.55W
Depth of water	48m
Vessel type	Cruiser
Vessel dimensions	47.4m (l), 7.46m (b), 3.8m (d)
Date of building	1908
Date of loss	8 May 1947

Circumstances of loss

The SS *Muirchú* was originally named *Helga II* when it was built by the Dublin Dockyard Company in 1908 as a fishery protection cruiser for the Department of Agriculture and Technical Instruction. The 323-ton cruiser was propelled by 130 horsepower, triple-expansion engines and was capable of attaining a speed of 9 knots. It measured 47.24m long and 7.46m wide. As World War I progressed and the heavy loss of Allied vessels continued, *Helga II* was requisitioned by the Royal Navy in March 1915. The "II"

Above: The *Helga* is best known for her role in shelling Dublin during the 1916 Rising. She was later used to transport British auxiliary troops during the War of Independence. Thereafter, the *Helga* was handed over to the newly established Irish Free State and renamed the SS *Muirchú*. (Courtesy of the National Maritime Museum, Greenwich)

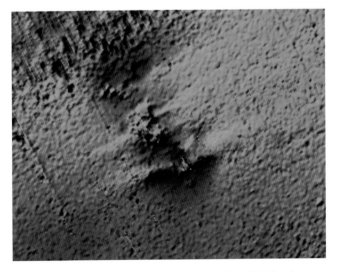

Above: Multibeam view of the broken-up remains of the SS *Muirchú* on the seafloor.

was dropped and the newly renamed HMY *Helga*, which was reclassified as an Armed Auxiliary Patrol Yacht, was fitted with a 12-pounder and a 3-pounder gun. For the duration of the war HMY *Helga* was based in Kingstown (now Dún Laoghaire), Co. Dublin, and was primarily engaged in anti-submarine patrols and escort duties in the Irish Sea and Celtic Sea.

During the 1916 Easter Rising, the *Helga* shelled rebel positions in Dublin city centre, including Boland's Mills, Liberty Hall and the Dublin Distillery. In February 1918 the *Helga* attacked a submarine off the Isle of Man, and even though the U-boat escaped back to its base, for the remainder of her career the *Helga* carried a star on her funnel as a reminder of this achievement. Another notable achievement of the *Helga* was its involvement in the rescue of 90 people from the RMS *Leinster*, which had been torpedoed and sunk, with the loss of 501 people, off the Dublin coast in October 1918. In 1919 the *Helga* resumed its fisheries duties and was transferred to the newly formed Free State government in 1922.

With the outbreak of the Civil War (1922–3), the *Helga* was commandeered by the Free State Army's Marine Investigation Department for coastal patrol duties. She was used in the transportation of Free State troops along the Munster coastline, and for bringing relief supplies to counties Galway and Sligo. The vessel was also used in the transportation of Republican prisoners from Donegal to Dublin. With hostilities coming to a close, the *Helga* was transferred to the Irish Free State's Department of Agriculture in May 1923 and earmarked for fisheries work. In August of the same year the vessel was once again recruited for naval duties, this time with the newly established Coastal and Marine Service, and renamed the *Muirchú*, after the 7th-century cleric and biographer of St Patrick. This naval service was disbanded by a cash-strapped government in March 1924, with the *Muirchú* returned to the Department of Agriculture to carry on with her task of fishery protection.

The outbreak of World War II saw the *Muirchú* being taken over by a new Marine and Coastwatching Service in December 1939, and refitted for her wartime task of anti-submarine patrols. Later in the war she was also used for mine-clearing duties. In 1947 the *Muirchú* was the first ship to be commissioned into the newly formed Irish Naval Service. It never saw service, unfortunately, and with the arrival of three Flower class corvettes, purchased from the Royal Navy, the 39-year-old cruiser was decommissioned. The vessel was sold for scrap to the Hammond Lane Foundry in Dublin, but foundered while on tow from Haulbowline to Dublin, 5.1km southwest of the Saltee Islands, in May 1947. There was no loss of life.

On the seafloor

The wreck of the *Muirchú* is orientated NW–SE and measures 48.5m in length, 7m in width and 3.6m in maximum height. It lies on its port side and is badly broken up, however one rather curious sight is that of a completely intact bath sitting amongst the wreckage. There is an area of deep scouring at the SE end of the wreck and aft the starboard propeller is missing a blade.

Printed Sources
Collins 2002
Larn & Larn 2002

Top: A diver investigates the deck area of the *UC-42* (see pp. 83–4), which lies on its starboard side in 27m of water off Roches Point, Co. Cork. (Photo Tom Brett)

Bottom: Divers investigate the mangled remains of the bow of the *UC-42* (see pp. 83–4). (Photo Tom Brett)

Appendix: Database of Wrecks

Vessel Name	Vessel Type	Date Of Loss	Water Depth (M)	Wreck Length (M)	Wreck Width (M)	Latitude	Longitude	GSI Ref.	NMS Wreck Number	Survey Cruise*
Rutland Island Wreck	Sailing Vessel	c. 16th Century	5	18	6	54.972	-8.444	299	W11641	Geo11_05
La Surveillante	Frigate	02/01/1797	34	43.55	11.21	51.704	-9.541	258	W08507	Cv07_02
Queen Victoria	Paddle Steamer	15/02/1853	16	17.5	7.5	53.360	-6.051	144	W00910	Con04/ Kry09_02
Sir Charles Napier	Sailing Ship	19/11/1857	8	30	7.5	53.262	-5.925	280	W01588	Kry10_01
Glenorchy	Sailing Ship	01/01/1869	7	69	13	53.281	-5.929	277	W01572	Kry10_01
HMS Vanguard	Ironclad Battleship	01/09/1875	45	104	16	53.213	-5.772	247	W02099	Cv08_03
SS Vesper	Iron Steamship	13/01/1876	9	54.8	7.8	53.268	-5.930	284	W01594	Kry10_01
Flying Dart	Paddle Tug	01/01/1890	28	28	5	53.347	-6.011	135	W00883/ W01549	Cv03_01
SS Premier	Steam Coaster	26/11/1898	22	53.4	8.3	52.592	-9.641	253	W06353	Cv09_01
Marlay	Cargo Vessel	16/12/1902	27	61	10.5	53.388	-5.977	249	W02049	Cv08_03
SS Manchester Merchant	Cargo Vessel	15/01/1903	11	157	18	52.095	-10.033	248	W05784	Cv09_02
HMS Audacious	Dreadnought Battleship	27/10/1914	60	112	27	55.471	-7.752	111	W07147	Ce04_02
HMS Viknor	Armed Merchant Cruiser	13/01/1915	83	124	28	55.585	-8.242	71	W07837	Ce03_04
RMS Lusitania	Passenger Liner	07/05/1915	88	241	46	51.412	-8.548	155	W08561	Calibration
SS Folia	Ocean Liner	11/03/1917	30	113.2	16.5	51.881	-7.689	274	W08274	Cv10_02
Antony	Passenger Ship	17/03/1917	57	133	20	52.002	-7.005	215	W03173	Cv01/02/03 Scallops
SS Bandon	Cargo Vessel	13/04/1917	33	81.9	11.5	51.949	-7.580	271	W04769	Cv10_03
Calchas	Cargo Vessel	11/05/1917	126	72	23	51.910	-10.831	134	W05584	Ce05_04
Saint Mirren	Sailing Ship	26/05/1917	178	90	21	55.915	-8.239	9	W07586	Ce03_02
Carthaginian	Passenger Liner	14/06/1917	54	116	21	55.448	-7.401	116	W07211	Ce04_04
Karina	Passenger Liner	01/08/1917	73	106	28	51.825	-7.047	223	W03818	Cv01/02/03 Scallops
Athenia (sunk 1917)	Passenger Liner	16/08/1917	54	148	43	55.555	-7.356	103	W07145	Ce04_02
Devonian	Passenger Liner	21/08/1917	75	170	28	55.503	-8.031	90	W07252	Ce03_05
Roscommon	Cargo Vessel	21/08/1917	73	137	17	55.490	-8.017	96	W07575	Ce03_05
Cooroy	Merchant Ship	29/08/1917	62	60	10	51.961	-6.933	224	W03357	Cv01/02/03 Scallops
UC–42	Submarine	10/09/1917	27	45		51.751	-8.215	275	W05519	Cv08_02
SS Etal Manor	Steam Collier	19/09/1917	58	93	19	52.003	-6.899	214	W04890	Cv01/02/03 Scallops/ Cv10_02
SS W.M. Barkley	Cargo Vessel	12/10/1917	49	54.5	8.3	53.372	-5.659	265	W02101	Cv10_01
U-58	Submarine	17/11/1917	78	60.7	8.4	51.606	-8.165	290	W10138	Ce10_018
Hare	Merchant Steamship	14/12/1917	65	45	10	53.400	-5.716	185	W02024	Cv01/02 Pad/ Cv10_01
Maxton	Cargo Vessel	28/12/1917	166	40	13	55.891	-7.987	14	W07487	Ce03_02
U-89	Submarine	13/02/1918	57	56	8	55.705	-7.580	276	W07703	Ce03_04
Amazon	Passenger Liner	15/03/1918	113	168	29	55.771	-8.189	33	W07115	Ce03_03
Myrtle Branch	Cargo Vessel	11/04/1918	58	112	19	55.6217	-7.2242	95	W07506	CE03_05
SS Fern	Passenger Ship	22/04/1918	76	54.2	8.2	53.4309	-5.7823	264	W02012	CV10_01

Vessel Name	Vessel Type	Date Of Loss	Water Depth (M)	Wreck Length (M)	Wreck Width (M)	Latitude	Longitude	GSI Ref.	NMS Wreck Number	Survey Cruise*
SS *Polwell*	Steam Collier	05/06/1918	30	96.2	11.5	53.5530	-5.9320	255	W02067	CV09_05
Justicia	Passenger Liner	20/07/1918	67	224	50	55.663	-7.720	58	W07410	Ce03_04
Flavia	Passenger Liner	24/08/1918	101	76	19	55.314	-8.991	119	W07330	Ce04_04
HMS *Guide Me II*	Drifter	29/08/1918	33	28.5	5.5	53.272	-6.054	138	W01482	Cv03_01
RMS *Leinster*	Passenger Ship	10/10/1918	28	112	15.5	53.314	-5.793	153	W02039	Cv05_03 Imagin
Athenia (sunk 1939)	Merchant Ship	03/09/1939	189	139	29	56.739	-14.375	112	W07146	Ce04_03
FV *Thomas Hankins*	Trawler	20/11/1939	96	54	N/A	55.386	-8.548	115	W07682	Ce04_04
HMS *Carinthia*	Armed Merchant Cruiser	07/06/1940	112	169	38	55.248	-9.300	131	W07682	Ce05_01
HMS *Transylvania*	Armed Auxiliary Cruiser	10/08/1940	129	182	27	55.812	-7.811	23	W07688	Ce03_02
Cumberland	Cargo Vessel	24/08/1940	55	152	33	55.526	-7.254	109	W07241	Ce04_02
City Of Simla	Cargo Vessel	21/09/1940	175	107	29	55.936	-8.165	6	W07230	Ce03_02
Kerry Head	Coaster	22/10/1940	69	52	25	51.498	-10.025	233	W08492	Ce06_01
Empress of Britain	Passenger Liner	28/10/1940	159	212	40	55.318	-9.683	1	W07307	Ce03_01
Veronica	Merchant Ship	17/11/1940	91	65	13.5	55.522	-8.646	80	W07834	Ce03_05
Bussum (After Part)	Merchant Ship	23/11/1940	131	57	16	55.802	-8.076	178	W09503	Ce03_02
Rask (Possible)	Merchant Ship	19/10/1941	77	68	10	52.169	-6.187	202	W04190	Cv01/02/03 Scallops
HMS *Curacoa* (Stern)	Anti-Aircraft Cruiser	02/10/1942	122	54	15	55.839	-8.635	22	W07242	Ce03_02
HMS *Curacoa* (Bow)	Anti-Aircraft Cruiser	02/10/1942	123	37	9	55.835	-8.640	21	W07242	Ce03_02
U-743	Submarine	01/09/1944	65	58	7.5	55.630	-7.432	93	W11716	Ce03_05
Empire Heritage	Tanker	08/09/1944	65	155	37	55.543	-7.717	87	W07306	Ce03_05
Pinto	Motor Vessel	08/09/1944	64	81	14	55.537	-7.716	88	W07551	Ce03_05
U-281	Submarine (Deadlight)	30/11/1945	67	41	7	55.591	-7.691	76	W10131	Ce03_04
U-778	Submarine (Deadlight)	04/12/1945	67	54	5	55.541	-7.480	100	W10144	Ce03_05
U-218	Submarine (Deadlight)	04/12/1945	57	65	7	55.500	-7.432	117	W10125	Ce04_04
U-149	Submarine (Deadlight)	21/12/1945	83	20	4.5	55.643	-8.060	62	W10121	Ce03_04
U-155	Submarine (Deadlight)	21/12/1945	70	52	5.5	55.571	-7.578	91	W10122	Ce03_05
U-2506	Submarine (Deadlight)	05/01/1946	67	62	5	55.517	-7.507	101	W10127	Ce03_05
U-1009	Submarine (Deadlight)	05/01/1946	55	46	6	55.525	-7.399	171	W10114	Ce04_02
U-2511	Submarine (Deadlight)	07/01/1946	66	65	10	55.579	-7.626	85	W10209	Ce03_05
MV *Bolivar* (Bow)	Motor Vessel	04/03/1947	8	6	2	53.268	-5.924	279	W09480	Kry10_01
MV *Bolivar* (Stern)	Motor Vessel	04/03/1947	9	84	17	53.268	-5.926	283	W09480	Kry10_01
SS *Muirchú*	Cruiser	08/05/1947	48	48.5	7	52.069	-6.585	272	W04039	Cv09_03
Unknown	Barge	Unknown	21	29.5	8	53.635	-6.065	127	W00471	Cv04_01/02
Unknown	Barge	Unknown	21	32	8	53.635	-6.064	127	W00472	Cv04_01/02

* Survey cruise refers to the INSS/INFOMAR cruise in which the wreck was surveyed, i.e. Cv09_03 refers to a cruise onboard the *Celtic Voyager* in 2009, leg 3.

Bibliography

Anon. 1799 *The Naval Chronicle: Volume 1, January–July 1799: Containing a General and Biographical History of the Royal Navy of the United Kingdom with a Variety of Original Papers on Nautical Subjects*. J. Gold. London.

Anon. 2004 *Forgotten Shipbuilders of Belfast: Workman, Clark & Co., 1880–1935*. Friar's Bush Press. Belfast.

Anon. 2005 'Briefings – Glenorchy', *Subsea* **121**, 5. Irish Underwater Council. Dublin

Anon. 2007 SS *Mendi* Archaeological desk-based assessment. Unpublished report prepared for English Heritage. Wessex Archaeology.

Ballard, R.D. 1995 *Exploring the Lusitania, probing the mysteries of the sinking that changed history*. Wiedenfeld and Nicolson. London.

Barry, W.J. 1919 *History of Port of Cork Steam Navigation 1815 to 1915*. In the *Journal of the Cork Historical and Archaeological Society* **25** (1).

Bishop, C. 2006 *Kreigsmarine U-boats 1939–45*. Spellmount Ltd. Stroud.

Bishop, L. 2003/2004 'The forgotten story of *Justicia*', *Subsea* **114**, 33–4.

Bishop, L. 2006 'Audacious Aftermath - Recalling a Sleeping Dreadnought', *Subsea* **123**, 16–21.

Bishop, L. 2010 'The Subterranean World of Transylvania', in *Diver*. Eaton Publications. Middlesex.

Bishop, L. & Louden-Brown, P. 2001 'Justicia', *990 UK Diving in Depth*. 990 Publishing Limited. Lancashire.

Bonsor, N.R.P. 1979 *North Atlantic Seaway: an illustrated history of the passenger services linking the old world with the new*. Vol. 3. Stephens. Cambridge.

Bourke, E.J. 1994 *Shipwrecks of the Irish Coast, 1105–1993*. Vol. 1. Dublin.

Brady, K. 2008 *Shipwreck Inventory of Ireland – Louth, Meath, Dublin & Wicklow*. Stationery Office of Ireland. Dublin.

Breen, C. 2001 *Integrated Marine Investigations on the Historic shipwreck La Surveillante*. University of Ulster. Coleraine.

British Admiralty 1918 *Antisubmarine Information August 1918*. Office of Naval Intelligence Compilation No. 14, 1918. Government Printing Office. Washington D.C.

Browne, K. & Stokes, R. 2009 Kish Shipwreck Search: Survey Report December 2009. Unpublished report held by the National Monuments Service Archive Unit, Department of Arts, Heritage and the Gaeltacht.

Chatterton, E.K. 1943 *Beating the U-Boats*. Hurst & Blackett Ltd. Essex.

Colledge J.J. 1968, rev. 2003 *Ships of the Royal Navy: The Complete record of all fighting ships of the Royal Navy from the 15th century to the present*. Greenhill Books. London.

De Courcy Ireland, J. 1983 *Wreck and rescue on the east coast of Ireland*. Glendale Press. Dublin.

Grant, R. 1964 *U-boats destroyed – the effect of anti-submarine warfare 1914–1918*. Periscope Publishing. Penzance.

Hepper, D. 2006 *British Warship Losses in the Ironclad Era 1860–1919*. Chatham Publishing. London.

Hocking, C. 1969 *Dictionary of disasters at sea during the age of steam, including sailing ships and ships of war lost in action 1824-1962*. 2nd edition. Lloyd's Register of Shipping. The London Stamp Exchange. London.

Kelleher, C. 2010 'The Rutland Island Wreck' Underwater Archaeology Unit Interim Report. Unpublished Report held by the National Monuments Service, Department of Arts, Heritage and the Gaeltacht.

Kelleher, C. 2011 The Rutland Island Wreck. In *Archaeology Ireland*. Vol. 26 No. 3, issue No. 97, 38–40. Archaeology Ireland Ltd. Dublin.

Kieran, E. & Hayden, B. 2011 *Archaeological Impact Assessment of Nearshore Pipeline Route Survey for ARUP on Behalf of PSE Kinsale Energy Ltd*. Licence Numbers: 10R109, 10D38. Unpublished report held by the National Monuments Service Archive Unit, Department of Arts, Heritage and the Gaeltacht.

Kieran, E. & Hayden, B. 2011 *Archaeological Impact Assessment of Offshore Pipeline Route Survey for ARUP on Behalf of PSE Kinsale Energy Ltd*. Licence Numbers: 10R109, 10D38. Unpublished report held by the National Monuments Service Archive Unit, Department of Arts, Heritage and the Gaeltacht.

King, K. 1977 'The Sinking of the S.S. Polwell', *Beam, Journal of the Irish Lighthouse Service*, **9** (2). Commissioner of Irish Lights. Dublin.

Kemp, P. 1997 *U-boats Destroyed, German Submarine Losses in the World Wars*. Arms & Armour Press. London.

Larn, B.T. & Larn R. 2002 *Shipwreck Index of Ireland*. Lloyd's Register-Fairplay Ltd. Surrey.

Lowth, C.F. 2002 'Shipwrecks around Dublin Bay'. In *Dublin Historical Record*, Vol. 55, No. 1 (Spring 2002), pp. 50–63. Old Dublin Society. Dublin.

Martin, R. & Craigie-Halkett, L. 2006 (2008) *Risdon Beazley: Marine Salvor*. Ashford Press. Southampton.

McGill, B. 2010 'Deep in the Northern Approaches', in *Diver*. Eaton Publications. Middlesex.

Miller, D. 2000 *U-Boats, history, development and equipment 1914–1945*. Conway Maritime Press. London.

Molony, S. 2004 *Lusitania: An Irish Tragedy*. Mercier Press. Cork.

Möller, Eberhard & Brack, Werner 2004 *The Encyclopedia of U-Boats, from 1904 to the Present Day*. Greenhill Books. London.

Niestlé, Axel 1998 *German U-boat losses during World War II, details of destruction*. Naval Institute Press. Annapolis, MD.

O'Donnell, B. 1999 *The Story of the Rosses*. Caorán Publications. Donegal.

Quinn R., Breen C. and Forsythe W. 2002 'Integrated geophysical surveys of the French Frigate *La Surveillante* (1797), Bantry Bay, Co. Cork, Ireland', in *Journal of Archaeological Science*, **29**, 413–22.

Rossler, E. 1981 *The U-Boat, the evolution and technical history of German submarines*. Arms & Armour Press. London.

Simpson, C. 1996 *Lusitania*. Avid Publications. Merseyside.

Smith, E.W. 1947 *Trans-Atlantic passenger ships, past and present*. George H. Dean Company. Boston.

Stokes, R. 1996 'The curse of Saint Patrick', in *Subsea* **83**. Irish Underwater Council. Dublin.

Tennent, A.J. 1990 *British merchant ships sunk by U boats in the 1914–1918 war*. The Starling Press Ltd. Newport.

Thomas, C. 2006 *Lamentable Intelligence from the Admiralty: The Sinking of the HMS Vanguard in 1875*. Nonsuch Publishing. Dublin.

Tierney, J. 2005 Diving U-89, in *Subsea* **119**, 14–15. Irish Underwater Council. Dublin.

Williams, D. 1997 *Wartime disasters at sea, every passenger ship loss in World Wars I and II*. Patrick Stephens Limited. Somerset.

Wilson, I. 1999 *Donegal Shipwrecks*. Impact Printing. Antrim.

Woodman, R. 2004 *The Real Cruel Sea – the Merchant Navy in the Battle of the Atlantic 1939-1943*. John Murray Publishers. London.

Wynn, K. 1997 *U-boat Operations of the Second World War. Career Histories*. 2 Vols. Chatham Publishing. London.

www.bruzelius.info

www.clydesite.co.uk

www.gwpda.org/naval/lusika00.htm

www.fleetwood-trawlers.info

www.irishshipwrecks.com

www.mightyseas.co.uk

www.mii.connect.ie

www.naval-history.net

www.theshipslist.com

www.teesbuiltships.co.uk

www.uboat.net

www.warsailors.com

www.wrecksite.eu

Index of Ship Names

Index